Acclaim for **This Is How We** [...]

'Wise, funny and profound vi[...] escapades and eulogies to th[...] actually reads like The Great Irish-American novel'
—Nick Kelly, BROADSHEET.IE

'I always feel like I'm on a road trip with Diebold when I read his stories—he can turn something as mundane as making a sandwich into an epic, emotional journey. His writing goes from deliciously funny to deeply poignant, sometimes in the space of a single sentence. All of his stories evoke a powerful sense of place. A few sentences in, and I'm transported.'
—Katie Byrne, IRISH INDEPENDENT

'With detours through celebrity, ballet and Kung Fu, David Diebold writes with honesty, warmth and hilarity about fatherhood, family secrets, life, love, loss and the perils of growing up'
—Shane Hegarty, DARKMOUTH, BOOT, THE IRISH (AND OTHER FOREIGNERS) FROM FIRST PEOPLES TO POLES

'Penned with dazzling panache and great wisdom, *This Is How We Dance* is both a survivor's tale and a survival manual for anyone who's gotten mixed up with the sticky business of families'
—Damian Corless, CHRISTY DIGNAM: MY CRAZY WORLD

'I'm sad as hell now and it's barely just past sunrise... Good work. ' —Willy Vlautin, MOTEL LIFE, LEAN ON PETE, NORTHLINE, DON'T SKIP OUT ON ME

'One of the cleverest and funniest writers I know'.
—Rowan Joffe, 28 WEEKS LATER, TIN STAR

This is How We Dance

DAVID DIEBOLD

Monument Media
Dublin, Ireland

ISBN: 978-1-9162531-1-7 (Paperback)
ISBN: 978-1-9162531-2-4 (eBook)
2 4 6 8 10 9 7 5 3 1

Acknowledgments
This book would have been impossible without Emily, improbable without Jonathan, and imperfect without Ruth McKee. Love and thanks to the family and friends who inspired every piece published here, especially Emily, Zach, Jona, Sammy and Jessica; Ollie G, Rob B and Paul D; John D, Max N and Peter C. Thanks also to Aidan Herron and Tom Reilly for their professional advice, and to Simon Hess for his, also Stephen Moore and Cyril Meehan.

Back cover author image by Adrian Brinton.
Design by Monument Media Ltd.

Printed by Turners, Longford, Republic of Ireland.

This book has been typeset in Adobe Garamond, a digital interpretation of the roman types of Claude Garamond (1480-1561) and the italic faces of Robert Granjon (1513-1589). Since its release in 1989, Adobe Garamond has become a typographic staple throughout the world.

First printing edition 2019.

Monument Media Ltd
18 Thomas Hand Street
Skerries, Co Dublin
K34 HH24

www.monumentmediapress.com

For Polly and Don

Twist for her, olive for him…

Contents

Foreword:
Both Sides Now

BY RUTH MCKEE

'We are torn between nostalgia for the familiar and an urge for the foreign and strange. As often as not, we are homesick most for the places we have never known' —Carson McCullers

We are made of stories. It's how we communicate and remember, how we build a sense of self; we inhabit them. In the best and worst times of our lives we reach for narrative to make sense of the world, of our experiences. There are as many stories in this collection as there are weeks in a year, and years in the author's life at publication; here you will find every emotional season, sometimes all in the space of one page.

In an interview for the *Los Angeles Times*, Kevin Barry said that one of the interesting things about Irish people is talk. "We talk a lot and say very little. It's what's going on under the surface of the talk that's interesting." *This is How We Dance* is a conversation: between the writer and the reader—those who picked up The Herald newspaper each week to read a familiar columnist talk about his episodes in fatherhood, his haphazard navigation of modern life, from which these pieces are gleaned; it's also a dialogue between family and friends, both past and present—and at its most poignant it's a conversation the author has with himself.

Humour subverts expectations; it's a way of seducing the reader. Funny is the low hanging adjective to describe this book, because it is—these pieces give you a wry smile or a bark out loud laugh, as Diebold is expert with the wisecrack, the one-liner and the deadpan observation. He has an easy style; it's like sitting in the bar with an old friend as he leans forward to tell you something about last summer, or what happened to him on the way to the station. But there is also depth and gravity, albeit by the side gate. Diebold invites you in with a joke, but often leaves you with his hallmark change of key, taking you from major to minor in the length of a thousand words.

Happiness is here in abundance, in the small and large things: the glitter on a card made by a child; the smell of homecooked burgers; the freedom of the road. There are those relatable moments in life: watching your child grow up, and letting them go; falling in love; finding a friend. But there are also things unique to the author, a family history so unusual and complex it is worthy of a documentary—yet you never feel on the outside. The stories that explore the stranger aspects of his background feel as natural and close as those set in the supermarket on the main street of Skerries, Dublin, where Diebold lives. This is his talent—making the particular universal, and the universal particular.

There is looking up, and looking forward in this volume—on father-son mountain climbs as a child, into cold January skies, the advice and admonitions of his father keen in the writer's mind decades on, in *Fellow Misanthropists*. We stay on the mountain for a more ridiculous climb years later, as Diebold and his belly struggle to keep up with his long-time friends in the hilarious *Climb Any Mountain*.

There is looking down, and looking back too, as friends arrive, and friends disappear. Sometimes it's via a chance meeting—maybe a couple of beers with a successful novelist, or a fleeting encounter with a musician, people and times now vanished; elsewhere it's by paying homage to those treasured people who have left the show. There are castles in the air, as ambitions and jobs change as quickly as cities and circumstances. There are clouds too. Diebold describes a childhood honeyed with the nostalgia of quarry roaming and afternoon television in *Kung Fu Kid*, but also hints at a psychological burden that would take a novel to examine. Yet even the most difficult subjects are written with a light touch. It's a fairground of memories, from rollercoasters to games of chance, to the slow circle of a Ferris wheel.

There is no misery to this memoir, despite it tackling grief—the thing with feathers—that settles in the author in the middle of his life, considered with subtlety in *Nick Cave Nails It*. Loss, like love, is given the same cadence, with crescendos and diminuendos, as is family life in all its mess and glory: family, despite Diebold's comical lamentations, is the one constant in the flux and flow of everything else.

The author is often characteristically flippant when dealing with painful questions, or sensitive periods in his life; at times you hanker for more of the straight man, for the writer who has left the mask of columnist and raconteur down for a while. Possibly the volume is at its most powerful on those rare occasions we glimpse the author's face when the audience has left the room—evident in the concluding story, *Secrets*.

Ultimately, Diebold wants to leave us laughing, not to give himself away—or at least not too much. Because in the end what is it, this beautiful, chaotic, epic of a life, if not, in the words of the incomparable Bill Hicks, just a ride: and that's precisely what this collection is, from up and down, from give and take—a dizzying, dancing ride.

Ruth McKee *writes reviews for Irish Times Books, and works for independent publisher Doire Press. She is the creator and editor of www.spontaneity.org, an interdisciplinary arts magazine, which began in 2014.*

About David Diebold

David Diebold has written for *The Irish Independent, Irish Daily Mail* and for *The Herald,* where his regular weekly column of seven years made the judges' shortlist for the National Newspapers of Ireland Feature Writer of the Year award in 2011, and NewsBrand Ireland Popular Columnist of the Year in 2016. His writing featured in *Press Gang, Tales from the Glory Days of Irish Newspapers* (New Island, 2015), and in *Spontaneity* magazine. A collection of his weekly parenting columns *The Family Guy* will be available as an Amazon eBook titled *Diary of a Wimpy Dad.* A native of California, he lives by the sea, near Dublin, Ireland, with his wife and four children, and up to six dogs at any given time.

This Is How We Dance

To the tune of Aztec Camera's *Oblivious* from secret speakers somewhere behind the fruit: she takes a basket from the stack, I take it from her then hand it back, she rolls her eyes.

We do a two-step past the avocados. I lead, she's two steps behind. I used to waltz her on my feet, hold her tiny hands to some Lucinda Williams song. Now I want to ask her *ever felt like setting fire to the world just to see what's real?* Instead, I say—Bananas? and she shrugs.

I let my footwear dictate the dance and march, *Paso Doble*, to the meat counter, skidding to a halt with a bullfighter flourish. She melts behind a pillar of sauces. I double back, tip-toeing up behind her and tapping her on the shoulder. She glares.

I mince my way back to the meat, shopping basket between thumb and forefinger like a handbag. I pick up a wrapped tray of lamb kidneys.

1

—Do these chicken breasts look a little dark to you? I say, all mock-concern. She whips her head away and stomps out of view.

It's just how we dance.

I find her by the cereal, a portrait of exasperation.

—Oh, hello, I say. Fancy meeting you here.

—Can I have the keys to the car? she says, eyes shut tight.

—Nope.

I pluck a box of flakes from the shelf and hold it like a percussionist shaking a maraca. She wrenches the cereal away from me, putting it back.

—No cereal? I say.

—I don't even like cereal. Her face is turned away now.

This is how we dance.

I turn the corner to another aisle, run halfway down and stop, pretending to browse a shelf. When she sees me, it's as though I've appeared there by magic. She walks towards me, I move away, looking over my shoulder nervously, as though I'm being followed by a complete stranger, then I stop.

—Can I help you with something, miss? I say.

—Just give me the keys. Her face is pained. I'm serious.

—Nope.

—I'm never going shopping with you again.

This is how we *used* to dance...

I'd hold out my hands: *climb me like a tree.* She'd lean back, use her feet to clamber up: we'd twirl round and around.

—How about bagels? I say. She likes bagels. Right?

A brief glimmer behind cloud. She takes off in the direction of the bread.

—Stop! I yell. She turns. I nod in the other direction.

—Aisle four. I'll get the cream cheese.

When she finds me, I'm singing into a refrigerated unit, something by Altered Images.

—There's something seriously wrong with you," she says, but she's smiling now. Can we go though? I'm *really* tired.

—Sure, I tell her, but I say it very slowly, like a record on the wrong speed, then I move off as if through water, slow-motion ballet with a brimming basket, boots squeaking on the linoleum—because this is how we dance.

—You're not even funny any more, she says.

We had an '80s disco in the front room one night. New Order, Tears for Fears, Duran Duran. It started as a joke, then we just kept dancing. She wore a little blue trilby hat back then; when you twirled her around she could still fit under your arm. Her mother knew the words to all the songs and she thought this was the funniest thing.

—I meant to get some chicken.

—I am not going back over there with you again, she says, her emphasis on the word *not*.

—I was going to make enchiladas.

—I'm really not hungry any more.

—They'll keep.

She folds her arms again and stares at the ceiling.

—That's okay. *I'll* go. I race away like an ice skater, giant boots screeching across the shiny floor—because this is how we dance.

I return to find her yawning at the check-out.

—That line is shorter, I tell her, moving to another queue. No wait, I say, and join a third. *Actually...* and I shuffle over to the self-scanning station.

I don't recall if a Dutch master ever painted a study in abject mortification, but if they did, its inspiration would

3

be, just out of frame, a man with giant wellies and a coat covered in dog hair.

But I can't help it, this way that I dance.

A boy in her year has asked her to the school dance.

—Well, I tell her as we load shopping into the car, of course, I had to do an entire background check on him.

—No you didn't, she says, but she sounds uncertain.

—Ten page report, I tell her, starting the car.

She laughs, just once, and catches it, an escaping butterfly in her hands.

I imagine her all dressed up on the night with her date, bright lights reflected in her clear eyes, and the question holds me: *Will they dance?*

Just Like Jack Nicholson

As a child, I considered my family situation unique. My life, before the truth came out, felt like an elaborate undercover operation, as if we had assumed identities on a witness protection programme, dad striking a Cary Grant figure, and my mother...

—She's not my real mother, I'd announce to the waitress, or to people at the next table, beaming baby teeth as mom curled into her fists before smiling apologetically.

—Where he gets these ideas, I don't know...

—My sister... I'd pipe up, high-pitched, bouncing on my seat. She's...

—Drink your milk, mom would say, pulling my chin towards her.

My sister was my real mother: that was the truth of it.

It wasn't so unique.

Much later, I learned that Jack Nicholson discovered the same thing about his 'sister', the same year I found out about mine. It was 1974; he was 37, and had just finished making the movie *Chinatown* when a reporter from Time magazine broke the news. I was seven, a yo-yo immigrant from America, having been moved to Ireland around the time of the Manson murders—Dad was sickened by violence of Los Angeles—drifted back, and then returned to Ireland again for good.

That's when my sister showed up out of the blue and told me the whole thing before her suitcases even hit the hall floor. Seven years: not such a long time to keep a secret.

—So, instead of coming from her tummy, Mom would return from the restroom to find me explaining to the waitress, having borrowed a crayon to illustrate a napkin, I came out of my…

Dad would be sitting nearby, nose in a paper, as the waitress grimaced and nodded like a dashboard dog.

If my sister was my mother, I never once wondered what mom and dad were. Mom was mom. Dad was dad. But my sister, she was my 'actual' mother, and if that wasn't a story worth telling every stranger, then I didn't know what was.

—Well, thanks a lot, mom would rasp at dad, snatching the crayon, giving the waitress a pained smile. It was a scenario I took pleasure in repeating, at the school gate, in shops, at bus stops. They say the truth will out. For me, it was a verbal diarrhetic.

Jack Nicholson's 'sister' and 'mother' died years before he found out the truth about who was who; he's since said how glad he is they kept their secret to the grave.

—I didn't have to deal with it with them. They were dead, he said.

I was fine with my truth, young as I was, but I think I

started to sense the fears and jealousies that lurked around my sister-mother's re-emergence. I favoured her company, making the trek from school to where she was renting, without permission. We moved house, I moved school and still I sought her out, until one day, she was gone.

The spidery letters and blotchy paintings I insisted on sending for the first years after she disappeared back to the States went for the most part unanswered. Years later, I found many of them in a scrapbook under mom's bed. It would be fifteen years before I would see my 'sister' again, by which time I had long stopped regaling people with our painfully complex family past.

The closeness we'd felt when I was seven was largely gone. I felt guilty spending time with her, sensing it upset Mom; I was cautious about being rejected again, sad about all the years without the easy intimacy that mothers and their children often have. We were never to recapture the magic and excitement of that first reunion.

Jack Nicholson is grateful his sister and mother never told him the truth.

Do I ever wish that everyone had kept their secrets?

Sometimes.

That child, at ease with the truth disappeared for a while.

Later, I walked away from jobs and relationships that were flourishing: better to dump them, before they dumped me. But that's the great thing about growing up: eventually you stop blaming the bad decisions you make on the things that happened to you.

That's still my ambition... to grow up.

Someday.

Barefoot Kitchen Two-Step

Our bedroom door opens and a long shadow rides the spike of dull light from the door-frame as it travels across the bare boards, up the side of the bed and over the covers to where I'm squinting.

—What?

—I didn't say anything, comes the voice, fogged from sleep.

Once I realise it's our teenage daughter, I slip back under pillows like a swimmer turning beneath the surface of a warm pool for another lap. It's not unusual for one of the kids to creak in and thump across to the bathroom to use our electric shower, especially if it's early and the heating hasn't kicked in.

Treading water just below the surface, I wait for the *thump-thump-thump* past the foot of the bed, but it doesn't come. I'm conscious of a muffled exchange, so I stick my head up to hear.

—It's just history, the girl's voice is tired, thick with the cold. And I'd rather do the work at home on the computer or something.

—No, says her mother. You're going.

The door slams making the blinds twitch and I notice light seeping in. *Thump-thump-thump*. Another door slams somewhere else followed by a noise like things falling over on a desk, or junk being emptied from a tin.

—It's a school trip to a museum, explains my wife. And I really think she should go.

There are times when I might gently argue on the side of the girl, but I picture bright young teens craning their heads at glass cases and the thought of our daughter alone in the house all day seems too miserable.

I stagger to standing, scrabbling for soft, baggy morning clothes, burying my bed-hair in a hoodie. I'm not normally so motivated this early, but I sense a pivotal moment somewhere in the ether and think I may just be able to save the morning vibe… not like Superman, more like one of those comic book characters from the bottom shelf where they don't sell quite as well.

In the kitchen I settle on Thelonius Monk for the turntable.

Snap, crackle, pop.

The barefoot kitchen two-step is a practised dance, part ritual: counter top to coffee machine, to bin, to sink, and back. And so we court the day. A balance must be struck, a note, but you have to put something in before you get something back. Coffee beans are bitter, inedible, and the nasal roar of the grinder is nerve-shredding, but all is forgiven by the coffee machine's first delicious gasps.

I wipe down a board and assemble bread, cheese, ham, lettuce, tomatoes; jars of mayonnaise and pickles, ready for action. *Be the change you wish to see in the world*, Ghandi never said. Still, if I pause for a second, sip from this cup and listen to this music, perhaps I can at least change the bit of the world I can see from out of this hood.

It's all going to be down to the sandwiches...

I look at the components. I imagine my daughter floating between displays in the huge museum, hungry but then feeling a little lift when she remembers the sandwiches. I picture her smiling as she unwraps the silver foil and examines one of the triangles before taking a bite.

At the top of stairs, I knock on a door with a sticker on it that depicts a unicorn and the words *Feel the Energy!* This actually means *Stay Away*!

—WHAT! fumes a voice on the other side.

—Coffee, I tell it. The door opens just enough for a bare arm to appear and take the cup.

The art to the perfect sandwich is part flavour, part texture. Good bite. Nice crunch. Ham, cheese, tomato, cucumber. Chop, chop, chop. To use tomatoes you must first scoop out the insides, using only the firm flesh, the same goes for cucumber.

—Hi, she says, appearing, fully dressed. This is a good sign. The coffee must have worked. She frowns: Why is your hood up?

Good construction is vital. Once the components of the filling are chopped, they're mixed with just enough mayonnaise to bind them. More mayo is spread evenly to the edges of the bread—adhesive and waterproofing, but not too thick. Butter? Redundant. For heat, a dash of mustard or hot sauce (she'd say no if you asked, but what does she know?).

The filling is spread evenly, all the way to the crust, then a few crunchy leaves of Iceberg lettuce are finally layered on for crunch before the roof is attached with its own coat of adhesive and waterproofing. Cutting it into two triangles then enables an efficient delivery device. Pointy bit to mouth. It's a no-brainer. Last thing you want to do is stab yourself in the forehead with a blunt sandwich.

—Can I go now? she says. If you must, I say. She glowers, grabs her lunch and runs.

There's a comfort in remembering throughout the day that you may have changed the course of things.

—How did it go? I ask when she gets back from the trip in the late afternoon.

—Boring, she says, but at least we all got to go to Eddie Rockets to eat.

She tosses her bag on the counter and disappears.

I fish the parcel out of the bag and carefully peel open the foil to reveal the perfect sandwich.

Kung Fu Kid

I was a latchkey child, and I revelled in it.

From the minute my mom worked that loop of knotted nylon cord over my head, her eyes wincing from the smoke in the corner of her mouth, yanking on the thing to make sure it was secure, my life took a different course.

I would be king of the house each day after school.

She waved away a plume of smoke.

—Now let me see you open the front door.

The cord was too much of a pain to take off again, so I stood on the tip of my toes, extending the loop from my neck to the point where I made an involuntary choking noise as I turned my head to where the key finally slotted in and I could turn it.

—Very good, she said.

As the door swung open it took me with it, hanging by my neck and trying to keep up with it, tapping out a tight semi-circle on the toes of my shoes, like a ballet dancer staggering forward in the throes of some sort of dramatic death scene.

—Now, when you get home from school, you let yourself in, like you just did, and you do your homework. She emphasized the last three words like each one ended with a full stop and the next began with a capital letter.

Dad worked all day at the Evening Press. Mom had just got a job at a florist, a whole bus journey away. I clambered upstairs to my room, still coughing a little from the smoke and from my brief dangle from the door, to plan my next day.

Normally, I'd come straight home, more or less, depending on what dogs I met on the way, then I'd eat a sandwich, do as little homework as I could get away with, then beg to be allowed to watch TV.

The show I badly wanted to watch was *Kung Fu*. David Carradine starred as the silent Shaolin monk who wandered the wild west, fighting bullies and righting wrongs, often chucking lethal bladed metal stars at his enemies.

This was the bit mom wasn't keen on.

—I don't think watching that stuff is very good for you, she'd cough. Go outside and play.

Outside meant two options: exploring the treasures of the vast abandoned building site down the street, or heading up the hill to the disused quarry.

I usually went alone, which meant I could hum the theme tune to *Kung Fu* as loud as I wanted, look for circular pieces of metal and fling them in a wide arc, starring in my own episode.

Now, however, I'd have the luxury of an entire house and two episodes of *Kung Fu*, back to back, all to myself. I could watch the TV from two feet away and eat my lunch right there on the rug.

And so began a whole new era. I basked in solitude, the warmth of the screen, so close to my face that my hair would sometimes crackle, the volume up full, shrieking along to the theme music each day through a mouth full of sandwich.

The best adventures begin with a revelation. *Kung Fu's* Caine left the monastery when his Master was killed; he went in search of a long lost brother in order to settle down in the wild west. As a child I knew the truth about my sister—that she was really my mother. Years later, when I finally left Ireland, it was to start a new life in California, but also to find my real father.

His name was Bill. When I found him, he was working in the television and motion picture industry, making lighting effects for some of Hollywood's top production studios, including Burbank, where *Kung Fu* was filmed.

We whizzed past the security booth in his car on a whirlwind tour of the studio not long after we met, the half brother I'd never known in the back seat.

—No, said Bill, when I asked him. I never met David Carradine."

A few years later, however, I did meet Carradine. I was back in Ireland again, at the Dublin premier of *Kill Bill: Vol. 2*, in which he played Bill. He was standing all alone in the lobby, looking lost, when I charged up to him and seized his hand.

—Every day, after school, I babbled, pumping his arm. He looked at me, bemused, then I heard someone shouting and realised I'd just wandered into a photo session in front of the world's press.

Five years later, Bill—my Bill that is, or my real father, was killed by cancer, as though gunned down from behind by a baddie waiting in ambush.

When it was over, I remember turning on the TV for escape, and there was David Carradine, in all his *Kung Fu* glory, but it was a news item this time.

He had died that very same day.

Willy Vlautin Scrabbling at the Blinds

I tend to get a little over-excited in the company of successful novelists. This may go some way to explain why a cloud passes over the eyes of Willy Vlautin as I shuffle forward, looking over him in the queue to get my books signed, waving two of them at him like they're the sort of short planks one of his alcohol-addled characters might use to beat someone unconscious in a parking lot, strewn with broken glass behind a dead-end Reno dive bar.

—Dave, he says with what might well be a smile, but in such a way that could just as easily mean *oh, shit*.

—Dude! I awkwardly reach out for a man-hug impatient fans in the line, now snaking away in two directions, bore holes into me.

I haven't read *Don't Skip Out On Me* yet, but from what I could gobble up in the queue, it's about a boxer who, one can only assume, will turn out to be the sort of life's lottery loser that populates any number of songs on the eleven

17

albums Willy's band Richmond Fontaine has put out.

The book also contains a CD of music inspired by some of the dark situations within its pages. Willy played a few tracks earlier, in his mammoth two-hour publicity session at Whelan's, Dublin's famous music venue, detouring just once in tribute to the late, legendary *Herald* movie critic George Byrne with a beautiful and brittle version of *Post To Wire*, which quickly had those of us who knew George in tears. It was George who introduced me to Willy fourteen years before and I had been insinuating myself into the infuriatingly-talented man's company ever since, once even tracking his band to a Belfast gig and insisting on joining them for noodles after barging into a sound check. But by then Willy would've been used to me showing up without warning. Some years before, I'd somehow browbeat him into revealing his US cellphone number, probably with the understanding that I'd quickly misplace it.

However, not six months later, I found myself in Willy's home town of Portland, Oregon, with his number, now tattered and almost translucent, still burning a hole in my wallet. I really had no choice but to call.

No one could have been more gobsmacked than me when a gruff voice answered, quite different from the hitched and vulnerable voice Willy uses on stage.

—It's David, I said. David from Dublin.

There was a lengthy pause, during which I was sure I would hear the sound of a phone being slammed down.

—Oh, Dave! said Willy finally, with a more familiar enthusiasm. Where the heck are you calling from?

—I'm outside your house, watching you through your window, I joked.

—What? I imagined him instinctively ducking and scrabbling at the blinds.

—I said I'm just downtown. You told me to look you up. Wanna grab a beer or something?"

Arrangements were hastily made, to my surprise, during which I randomly stuck a pin in a map and chose what looked like an easy place to pick him up, then I scuttled off to squawk and flap my arms at my wife in excitement.

I was actually in Portland to visit my birth father, a Harley-riding, gun toting, special effects explosives expert named Bill, who insisted I borrow his pimped up Ford Expedition, a gas-guzzling beast that required driver and passengers to clamber up a ladder into a towering cab. It was, for all intents and purposes, a monster truck.

The location I'd randomly chosen turned out to be an expo centre where the controversial Body Worlds was on, a hellish museum of human meat mannequins, its soaring banner emblazoned with a bug-eyed corpse flayed of flesh beneath which awaited a rather nervous looking Willy Vlautin. I took a corner too tight, narrowly missed a fire hydrant and came careering towards him on bouncing wheels like some sort of crazed stunt driver, peering out some ten feet above, eyes wide and sweating like a lunatic, as I wrestled the steering wheel.

Had Willy decided at that moment to simply spring away over cars, as though prompted by gunshots, I probably wouldn't have blamed him, but inexplicably, some nail-bitten minutes later, we were screeching and bouncing to a stop together outside a nearby Thai place.

Over beers, I decided to lighten the mood by telling him about the time I'd convinced bestselling Irish thriller writer John Connolly to have dinner at Shanahans on the Green: the idea had been to have bloody steaks in the company of a mind that had invented some of the most gruesome deaths to ever spatter the pages of crime fiction.

—How did that go? asked Willy, tapping his beer bottle.

—Not as well as this.

I told Willy that just at the start of what would end up being a four-hour, six hundred euros, blow-out meal, I'd been so expressive in my storytelling that I'd sent an entire glass of full-bodied red across the white tablecloth.

—It looked like someone had just been slaughtered by a blow to the head from a mower blade.

—Jesus. Willy took a sip of beer, shifting in his seat. Then what?

—That, I couldn't help threatening, is a story best kept for another day.

Ice Cream in Italy

You know you're getting on a bit when the kids won't come on holiday any more.

Perhaps if I said we'd all be night-trekking through a jungle to bungee-jump over a waterfall, we might get more than a *nah*.

But it's not excitement they crave. If we could guarantee no traipsing around galleries or ruins, that the entire vacation would be spent slobbing around in sun loungers somewhere with Wi-Fi and waiter service, their bags would already be packed by the door for July.

As it is, we're down from a family of six to just three. We shouldn't complain. With just half of us going, we can go further, stay longer, and spend more money on art galleries and ruins. And wine. Let's not forget wine.

We settle on Nice. The flights are cheap and direct, we speak a bit of the lingo (in so far as I could probably tell anyone whether or not my uncle owns a pen, at least to

Leaving Cert standard) and there's the fact that we've been there before.

Thirty years ago, I followed my girlfriend of just a few short weeks when she left for the Cote d'Azur to work as an au pair. I knew if I didn't go, we would probably never survive a year apart. In 1987, mobile phones and internet were the stuff of science fiction and long-distance calls were virtually impossible when you lived on your own in a flat with a coin-operated phone down the hall.

Whether I'd have still gone all that way, had someone told me that I'd end up waking up beside a drug dealer, or that I'd be held at gunpoint by soldiers wanting to know if I was a communist, I might have just stayed working at Abracababra—and our four children might not exist today.

—Oh, not this story again, says my wife as I get to this point in a recent dinner-table reminiscence.

—I don't know what on earth you mean, I say, pretending to be somewhat hurt.

I've found myself on the wrong side of a heavily armed soldier several times in my life since—in Colombia, and in Liberia—but I've never had one see me off on a train with the wave of a hanky afterwards, and I'm pretty sure I've never told our four about it, but the conversation moves on and I let it go.

As we're clearing the table, I find a little Kodak booklet of snaps my wife dug out from all that time ago. I turn the crinkly pocket pages to find myself, almost the same age our eldest is now, looking very 1980s in my white grandfather shirt, trendy trouser braces and Sony Walkman, surrounded by palm trees.

It was this time of year, I remember. We'd just spent St Patrick's Day at a place in the old town called Hole

In The Wall—or *Ole In Ze Wull*—where a French singer murdered *The Green Fields Of France*. Low on cash, that night I decided to take my chances sleeping outdoors on my own on the beach. I stalked the Promenade Des Anglais until I found a suitable spot, tucking myself against the sea wall and trying to stay warm until the gentle fizz of the waves lulled me into unconsciousness.

In the morning, I woke to find a sleeping bag next to me with hair spilling out of it. The hair came alive with a yawn and a hand emerged outstretched.

—Morning, old boy, Harvey's the name, said a voice in perfect public school English.

Harvey, as it turned out, was a hoot. He bought us breakfast and told me how he'd dropped out of Oxford to play gigolo to a married heiress from Monte Carlo. The girl had broken it off and now he was getting by quite comfortably by selling hashish to tourists.

He must be, I decided between mouthfuls of pain au chocolat, the kindest and most articulate drug dealer ever.

That day, I scraped together enough cash to chip in on train tickets with my girlfriend to go up the coast to the tiny town of Ventimiglia, Italy, the equivalent distance of a DART ride to Bray. When we got there, however, the ticket collector wouldn't let us leave the station because we'd forgotten to bring passports.

—We just want an ice cream in Italy, I tried to explain.

—You go back to France, he barked, summoning two soldiers to keep an eye on us for the hour until our return train.

The soldiers had dark blue uniforms with white sashes and were armed with semi-automatic rifles. I was wearing a green bomber jacket with Soviet-style badges that I'd bought from a stall on O'Connell Bridge because, well, the Eightees.

One of the soldiers gestured to the badges.

—Comunista?

I shrugged.

—You come with us, he said, nudging us into the underpass beneath the train tracks.

I stood there in the semi-dark, the smell of soft, warm rain outside, as one soldier stood behind us and the other adjusted the gun on his shoulder and took out a cigarette. This, I thought, is where my girlfriend watches as I receive a rifle butt to the face.

The soldier thrust his hand at me and I winced.

—Comrade, he said.

—So what's there to do in Nice anyway? asks our daughter, finding me still staring at the photo.

—Oh, there are all kinds of art museums and churches to see, I tell her, watching her face drop.

—Great, she says.

—But we could always take a train trip to Italy on one of the days, I say looking back at the picture, just to have some ice cream.

Neatly Folded Bones

In a seething torrent of faces that whirls in currents or eddies into pools, the crowd moves towards the church door. Here, I'm stopped, and turn on tiptoe to survey the way I've come. Perhaps it's not so surprising that the eyes I latch on to, and that seem to latch on to mine in the same moment, are eyes that I think I recognise, though it's probably 38 years since we were in sixth class together.

The current pushes against me and I just have time to raise my eyebrows and give him a quick flick of my chin, as though using it to knock a small invisible ball his way, which I think he immediately returns in the same way, before I'm swept inside and directed up the aisle to one of the few remaining seats.

I pull my knees together so as not to make contact with the strangers on either side, then I crane my neck to look around and see if there's anyone else I recognise: other children's eyes trapped inside the slightly sagging, greyed masks of middle age. I squint and frown, then look away each time someone turns to squint and frown in turn at me. We're magic jigsaws of our younger selves; pictures hidden within muddled pictures.

My eyes find safety in the ceiling, where the beams reach high and clasp together like arms and hands in some memory of a playground game—chanting, chanting, chanting until that hand-held bell would ring.

There were twenty four faces in our final class photo. I remember the names of every one—names recited every day at roll-call; days that went on for years, back when the summer holidays lasted a lifetime, before we dispersed to new schools, like so many dandelion seeds exploding into the warm air. The friend-behind-those-eyes and I would kick our way through fields, to the nearby hill to build our forts, schoolbags slung into the ditch—behind the high wall to the park that bordered our walk home together.

Those same eyes, that same flick of the chin below a cheeky grin, *let's see how far off the path we can go*. Through hidden ruts between high ferns we went, the comforting shush of the canopy overhead, the dark yawn of some sort of cave between the thistles where we'd never been.

Then the smell of something old as we squatted and looked: the folded bones, brown, not like bones are supposed to look, but neat, as though drawn together for some final comfort.

We ran—until the woods opened out into sunlight and the beach fizzed far below. I was only pretending to be scared, honest, only pretending to be crying; only pretending to want so badly to go home now, swear.

—It was just a horse. Some poor horse fell down a hole, that's all, he laughed, catching up.

—I want to go home, I told him, pushing him away.

We didn't see each other again for a while. The roof of stick and ferns we'd laboured over all summer fell in, the biscuit tin of maps hidden beneath, lost somewhere under the mulch.

It was six months or more before I heard about the body of a woman found by Cubs as they played Hide And Seek around the hill on a field trip.

—Don't be so stupid, he said when I told him. That wasn't it. That wasn't what we saw. It was a horse. Just some stupid horse.

I never mentioned it again.

Most of my classmates went on to different schools. Seeds scatter on their tiny parachutes, blown by various winds, many settling far apart before taking root there. Some flower and flourish, some struggle, most survive. But they're never again as they were in that first, perfect, impossibly delicate sphere.

High in that vaulted ceiling, is a single feather-like parachute, impossibly out of season and buoyed upon silence; the rector mounts the podium and adjusts his microphone.

—We're here to remember... he says. If you will all please now stand... And we remember, *we remember*...

Afterwards, I search the crowd outside for the pair of eyes I'd seen earlier, the same eyes that had squinted with mine into a dark hole on an unexplored side of the hill at the end of summer, when perhaps we only mistook old branches for neat, brown bones.

Perhaps I mistook those eyes today, too. All I know for sure is of the twenty four of us in that old class photo, one is gone forever, the reason why we're here, and it's rather like a child has died. Because that's how I remember him—not small, but the same size we all were together when we knew each other across classroom tables in the shadow of that hill, when our imaginations were our whole world.

And of all the things that might be lost or misremembered from those final summers of childhood, it's his laugh, pure and incorruptible now, that will stay with me until I too am nothing more than neatly folded bones.

JD the DJ

I can almost count my real friends on two hands. This is as it should be. It leaves room for an industrial accident like the one my uncle had when he lost a thumb and kept it in a bottle for years while the settlement worked through the courts.

I could pickle two thumbs, still count my friends, and have a finger left on each hand to pound out their stories. It's all in the fingers, see. A two-fingered typist with two spare thumbs and six long-time friends.

It's 10 years since I last saw him when I call JD out of the blue.

—Pint? This is how we do it.

—Yep. He's not being brusque.

—How's that young lad of yours? I say. One of the last times I saw JD was at his fiftieth, in The Ginger Man pub. His son was ten but knew how to talk rock music. I gave the boy a wallet I kept on a chain.

—He's about to go into his fourth year in Trinity, says JD. Philosophy.

I try to take this in.

I was twenty when I met JD. The travelling theater group we found ourselves in was like The Commitments. We were driven to succeed, driven in a Hi-Ace van as it happened, but only so long as we made it back to the dole office in time to sign on.

JD was our stage manager. He was also the gorilla. *When I accepted the job, I was sure I'd be playing the part of Che Guevara*, he'd say before pulling the giant fuzzy mask over his face and pummeling his chest.

Sometimes we didn't have time to change out of our costumes. Once we joined two hikers at a pee stop as they gazed over a bog doing their business; JD was in full gorilla get-up—the two stopped like water fountains cut off in mid flow. When the two were recovered enough to finish the job at hand, we gave them a lift to Galway. They were Irish music legend BP Fallon and Waterboys band member Anto Thistlethwaite.

—Who needs drugs with people like you around, grinned Beep.

A few years later, I bumped into JD on a journalism course. I walked into the lecture room and there he was.

—Well, whaddya know, I said, slapping him on the back side. Looks like we're on the same course.

—Well, of course. We would be, wouldn't we, he dead-panned, without missing a beat. He glanced around as the benches filled with students and put a finger to his lips, winking, and whispered—*Only thing is, I'm your lecturer.*

Within weeks, the two of us had started a newspaper. *Dublin News* was based in a then quite different Smithfield, populated by truck drivers lining up for heart-attack breakfasts amid boarded up windows and tumbling empty crisp bags.

From the start, it was clear we were to be a unique breed of free sheet. I was sent to take the mickey out of bike gangs and received death threats for my efforts. I went to Russia on holiday, got caught up in the Soviet coup and we ran three pages on it. The whole thing ended abruptly because we had no money. Our alcoholic ad salesman said advertisers preferred pieces on pooches, not putsches.

I drifted to the States and didn't see JD until we'd been back in Ireland for a while. I was editor of an entertainment magazine for one of the national dailies by the time I asked him to be godfather to one of our sons, Jonathan.

—You do know my name is not an abbreviation of Jonathan, he confided. And I'm an atheist.

—You do know we didn't name him after you, I said. And God's not invited.

He drove five hours to be there and five hours home the same night.

The only other time I'd seen JD was at his birthday in The Ginger Man and I'd gone alone because my wife had just given birth to our daughter. She's now seventeen.

—How does time go so fast? I ask him on the phone.

—Well, he tells me, when you were ten, a year lasted a long time because it was a tenth of your life. When you're fifty, a year is only a fiftieth. Relative to your experience, it seems a much shorter time.

As we pull in to his street, I savor the excitement of seeing him. One of his kids, now in her early twenties, is behind the counter, but I don't recognize her yet. She fetches him and when I turn around again he's filling the doorway.

31

Once we've completed the ritual of cursing each other then philosophizing over beers for an hour or three, I let him get back to doing what he has to do, which tonight is preparing for his set as DJ.

—DJ? I'm amused.

—DJ, he says, his eyes a dare.

I stay late to watch him in his element, mixing tracks like he's in Ibiza not West Cork; in the last changing flickers of colour and strobe light I take a final mental snapshot of his face, fingers punching the air.

I'm up, don't leave yet, comes the text mid-morning, but we're already hitting the road.

See you again soon, I text.

Course you will, he replies, and he's not trying to be funny or smart. Because even if it's another ten years, by that time a year will only have been a sixtieth of my life.

I spread my fingers in front of me and look at them.

A sixtieth is nothing.

Mad Max

About thirty years ago, I answered a small ad in *The Irish Press* to audition as an extra in the world-famous Kirov Ballet's production of *Le Corsaire*.

It was the fateful first step towards a friendship with one of the troupe that would one day find me hiding out on the border of Estonia during the Soviet coup of 1991—an experience that would, over many years, be consigned to the proverbial ha'penny place, in terms of the havoc that friendship would always trail in its wake.

Back in 1990, I couldn't even dance but needed the cash, so off I went to line out with the twenty or so other hopefuls who stretched and flexed in their leotards while I struggled to touch the toes of my Docs.

In marched Oleg Vinogradov, feared artistic director of the Kirov, trench coat over his shoulders like a cloak and trailing acrid smoke from his *papirosa*, a hard-core traditional Russian cigarette that smouldered on the end of a pinched cardboard tube. He scowled at each of us in turn, then pointed at the six tallest, barked something and left. I was in.

It was magic to have some of the world's best dancers leaping twelve feet in the air around you; when we weren't on stage, we were back in the green room playing snooker. The Russians loved their snooker, and none more than Kirov character-dancer Maxim Nisnevich, son of famed teacher Anatoli.

Security was tight for the duration of the Kirov's stay, even though political tensions had relaxed considerably under Gorbachev, so there was a bit of a stir when Max invited me onto the tour bus to go back to the hotel with the entire ensemble for a big party in one of the rooms.

Hired guards tried to escort me off, but Max was having none of it and threatened to take off with me up the dark quays, then began recruiting other Kirov members to join us. There was a brief stand-off, then the guards left, the bus rumbled to life and off we all went with a cheer.

Some months later, Max invited me by telegram to visit him in what was then still Leningrad. A few days after I arrived, hard-line communists attempted to take back control of the country from Gorbachev, something that would become known as the August Putsch of 1991.

As tanks began to roll and people took to the streets, Max thought it better we got out of dodge, so we legged it to his family dacha on the border of Estonia to wait things out.

It wasn't so bad. While air-force jets shrieked overhead, we combed local forests strewn with World War Two wreckage, fished, hunted, then drank shots of vodka in the comfort of traditional village steam-houses.

To the revolution, Max would cackle, raising his glass.

By the time we got back to Leningrad, it had become Saint Petersburg and the Soviet flags had been replaced with the traditional Tsarist white, blue and red, which we promptly waved from atop the nearest Lada, as though we'd carried the whole thing off ourselves.

I moved with my wife-to-be from Dublin to San Francisco within a year; Max came to visit us. He screeched up in front of our house in a white convertible and smashed into the back of our car, making it shudder forward—something which became a daily tradition for the duration of his stay, which stretched to a month, by which time both our cars were wrecks.

—Cars much better in Russia, he concluded every time he swapped back a damaged one.

We all went to Lake Tahoe together and almost sank a couple of jet skis, racing across the waves, Max shrieking like a maniac and trying his best to aim his machine at mine at breakneck speed. When we somehow made it back to shore alive, engines groaning for mercy, the rental man waded in.

—You guys are friggin' nuts, the guy said, and I'm from Nevada. We know *crazy*. Max took this as one of the greatest compliments of his life.

Wherever we went, things quickly got out of hand, even window shopping. Back in San Francisco, we got chased out of a camera shop by Turkish vendors wielding baseball bats after Max spent forty minutes haggling for discounts, only to admit he had no interest in buying anything. He just wanted to see how low they'd go. Three of them vaulted the counter and ran after us for half a mile.

A scene always ensued wherever Max was concerned, something which continued until a few years ago, when he turned up in Ireland out of the blue with a minor eye infection and insisted that we help him organise what he called his immediate 'emergency medical evacuation' back to Russia. Only if he could travel first class, of course.

From what I recall through clenched fingers, he got the upgrade. He sent a photo from a beach in Bali and the eye seemed better.

Last we heard, Max was eighty miles inside the Arctic Circle, approaching a rescue camp on his snowmobile. He stopped to post a selfie with the Aurora Borealis and to send us an ominous message: *see you soon*.

Fellow Misanthropists

The mountains seem closer now than they were when I was a young teen. This is not a physical fact, of course, though they may well have shifted an inch or two on their tectonic plates in the forty years since then—it's a purely relative thing.

In the early 1980s when I hiked with Dad, it took hours to shriek along the pitted motorways in our freezing little red Volvo Daf, then even longer to shudder along one-lane back roads where brambles whipped the windscreen to where we could finally pull in on some muddy bank and struggle over a slippery gate through cow pats to access our climb.

Today, those motorways are hurtling rivers of metal; you can zip along in warmth and comfort with the stereo on as the mountains loom. Even the back roads are teeming now; the muddy paths snaking upwards are well trodden, rather than aching as they once did with profound solitude.

If we saw another car at the gate or in some forlorn forestry park at the foot of our hills, Dad might even have turned the car around, cursing: *I knew we left it too late*. We never once climbed a mountain for the company of others. We were fellow misanthropists. The nearest acceptable company of another human being, other than each other, might have been the occasional waft of pipe smoke from a shepherd in a field so far across a valley that his flock looked like tiny white ants.

Dad never had an awful lot of friends, but he seemed to like me well enough. *If you break your leg*, he'd tell me, *wrap yourself in the space blanket and eat your Kendal Mint Cake while I get help*. The space blanket was a thin foil sheet we kept folded away in our backpacks; Kendal Mint Cake was a rock-hard slab of peppermint flavoured glucose. A hike could not proceed if one of us, usually me, forgot to bring either.

We had whistles too—the old-fashioned police kind, on chords around our necks. *Three short blasts every few minutes*, Dad instructed, *until I find you*. Years before mobile phones and GPS, these were our emergency location devices. They made a lonely sound in the fog on the few occasions we lost sight of one another. *Keep up*, Dad would say.

We took off every Sunday, regardless of the weather, sometimes in wind so strong you could lean into it almost horizontally, or in sheets of rain, or knee deep in snow. By age thirteen, skinny as a broom, I had calf muscles like Popeye's arms.

The mountains we climbed—mostly mountains, not hills—had names that evoked ancient, sleeping giants: *Djouce, Kippure, Mullaghcleevaun, Lugnaquilla*. They brooded in cloud, or seethed in gales. We had nothing but respect for them, and disdain for the occasional newbies we met, who were woefully kitted out for the task.

Dad bought sets of thermal underwear and checked to make sure I wore mine. Jeans were for fools, he said: *If it rains, it's all over.* We wore corduroys tucked into thick wool socks and layers of pullovers, then huge, matching Lord Anthony coats with mittens threaded through on elastic so the winds couldn't whip them away when we stopped to huddle over sandwiches and tea.

We reeked of the sheep fat we used for rubbing on our leather boots, for softening and waterproofing, and we had tall, pine walking staffs Dad had found, then stripped and waxed, for negotiating bog holes. If any of my friends had seen us, I'd have been mortified.

I can still see the mica crystals glittering in the mud at our feet as we squatted under the vast erratic boulder on the saddle between Maulin and Djouce known as *The Coffin Rock*, and Dad doling out sandwiches made from chopped Spam and Cheddar, mixed to a mulch, flattened by our packs, with so much English mustard, we'd be in fits of sneezes.

On particularly bitter days, the flask of black tea would be laced with gin. It was my first taste of alcohol, high in the heather, head reeling a little as I felt the warmth of it spread from my stomach into the veins of my arms.

I remember Dad and those hikes now, when January days are icy-cold and the skies clear and blue. *Ready for inspection?* he might say and I'd have to lay out my kit before we left. Space blanket, Kendal Mint Cake, whistle and spare socks. Then we'd jam black berets over our heads, throw our pine staffs into the back of the Daff and trundle off in a plume of exhaust.

He died on the 29th of December, 2013; a dark and

rainy day that would have been terrible hiking weather. I'd visited him that morning and spoke into his ear as he lay there with his eyes closed, his mouth open, breathing, and I told him about the crushed sandwiches and bitter tea beneath a boulder where there was nobody in the world but the two of us.

It's fitting that I was with someone that I'd recently resumed hiking with, this time north in the Cooleys and Mournes, when the phone call came that Dad had died. Just a few months before, I had shared the gory details of some of those hikes with Dad at home, while he was still well.

—Sounds like you've really discovered the secret to happiness, he smiled.

Climb Any Mountain

I often find it hard to catch up with friends. The phrase 'catching up' takes on a whole new meaning when slogging up an 850m mountain on a rare day out, the first such day in a year, sweat in my eyes as I struggle with the pace.

—I'm not so sure this is good for the baby, I announce, patting my belly.

—Nearly there, says someone.

—Nearly where? I puff.

—At the start of the walk, they say.

—You know, when you said we were all going out today, I thought we'd be getting legless. I didn't think that meant I'd probably end up losing the use of my legs for a week afterwards?

The last time we'd done something like this, the artist, the publican, his friend and my gut, I'd marvelled at the way I'd somehow been able to overtake them, how they sweated and toiled, panting hard while I kept good pace.

But when we got near the top of that mountain, the two usually healthiest of the gang, who seemed to be finding it all such hard work that day, unzipped packs to reveal one full to the brim with ice and cold beers, the other with cooking equipment and steaks. My pack had only a light spare anorak and a Mars bar. My bragging rights, rather literally, went up in smoke, though it seemed more than a fair trade, at least as far as I was concerned. No one seems to be feeling the pain quite like me today, however.

—If I'd known we were going all the way up, I groan, I'd have come better prepared.

—I've some spare water, says the publican.

—I meant oxygen tanks, Sherpas, a yak.

—You're doing enough yakking for all of us, quips someone else.

The rough, stone-cobbled path eventually gives way to something like steps, continuing up and up, seemingly endless, a staircase from hell, making my legs burn and my heart pound.

—Excuse me, pipes up a little voice, and a small girl in trainers tiptoes past, followed by her entire family.

—Lovely day for it, says the dad.

—I'm seventy you know, I shout after him hoarsely.

—And you don't look a day over sixty nine, he grins back over his shoulder.

—Honestly, I manage between breaths as the family disappears higher than I care to crane my neck. Mountain climbing is really no place to bring a child that small.

—Technically, we're just hill walking, chuckles the artist, but we'll go with mountain climbing.

—Oh, mountain climbing all the way, chimes in the publican.

—I hate you all, I say. Finally, we reach the saddle where

the Mourne Wall disappears each way into the distance, encompassing fifteen mountains in all. We stop to look back down the valley and I can't help being impressed with myself.

—Look, I pant. We're higher than that hill over there. I point. And that one too.

—Oh, they're hills now, are they? says someone. Everyone laughs.

—They're mountains when you're looking up at them, hills when they're down below, I inform them. Don't you know anything?

We consider this as we catch our breath, or rather, as everyone else catches their breath. Mine seems more elusive.

—Tell me that's the top, I say, squinting up to where the wall disappears over a ridge.

—That's the top, says someone.

They take off with renewed vigor and I struggle after, my legs blocks of wood on the broken stone. I suddenly remember something.

—Damn, I call after them. Forgot my phone.

—Don't think the rescue helicopter does tired climbers, I hear someone wisecrack.

—Don't worry I'll take a photo of you at the top," laughs someone else.

—No, I mean no step-counter total to post on Facebook—the whole walk is wasted, I snort.

—Wha'? You mean you haven't been counting yourself? You'll have to go back to the bottom and start again. They laugh. *One, two… wait. How many was that? D'oh!*

When I finally make it to the top of the ridge, everyone is waiting. I look up, gasping for air, to see the path continuing far up ahead to yet another ridge.

43

—I thought you said this was the top?

—Oh yeah. It is. It's the top of this bit.

—Just go on, don't worry about me, I wheeze, swatting the air with a limp hand. Worry about yourselves. You're the ones that'll have to carry me down.

—No, we'll just leave you here as a warning, says someone. I struggle to one side of the path as the little girl in trainers tiptoes back down past me, followed by her entire family again. Nice day f… the dad begins as he goes by.

—Don't even… I mutter. Just… don't.

I give up and sit down, shuffling up the steps backwards on my bottom for the final few yards to where I can already smell the coals smouldering underneath the home-made burgers someone packed.

It's hours and many pints later and dark by the time we finally say our good byes.

—It was good to catch up, I say.

—We knew you would, says someone. Eventually.

The (Very) Reluctant Adventurer

I have few mementos of my childhood. Where has all that treasured stuff that was stashed into cupboards gone? Probably a church sale sometime, long after I moved out of the family home.

Even the photos are few: isolated snapshots, often frizzy and faded; awkward family line-ups, usually one of us in a sulk, head resting on fists. I don't think of those times much. Our lives have been too busy stashing cupboards full of our own treasured stuff now, snapping our own fuzzy, fading memories.

Not long ago, however, I came upon a box, during one of those clear-outs of the attic, where you drag everything out with good intentions of a ruthless sorting between bin and charity shop, then get distracted by something you find, become utterly absorbed, then realise it's getting dark, so you just stuff everything back where it was again, less organised than ever.

This box was collapsing at the corners with age. When I looked inside, it felt like I was falling backwards out of a plane; my heart dipped, then soared.

There was a camping knife with a little folding spoon and, wrapped around it, a small braided length of fur from the dog we had when I was twelve, remnants of a time I hadn't thought about since Dad's funeral. Now, everything felt as hard and real as this folding metal artefact, heavy in my hand, as real as the still-oily length of knotted fur of a pet thirty eight years dead.

Dad and I had trained for months, slogging through the dark, granite-flecked mud of Wicklow. *After this*, Dad said, *it's the Pyrenees... then Kilimanjaro.*

We practised bivouacking, and concocted bowls of soupy instant mash, flecked with dead midges and tasting of plastic. There was something deliciously adventurous about unfolding that spoon with a satisfying click and shovelling up the grainy mash as the gas stove puttered between us.

Eventually, we took the ferry to Holyhead and the train to a ghastly guest house that smelled of carpets and cabbage. Dad made me lay out the contents of my backpack onto the bed, the clanking pots and packets of desiccated food, plastic plates and mugs.

—What's this? he said, unfurling a jumper to reveal a bundle of hardback books. You think we'll have time to *read?* He made me leave them behind. Where we're going, he said, we won't need books.

I opened one of them and slipped out the braid of thick dog fur I'd made into a lucky bookmark and I stuffed it into the pocket in the arm of my Lord Anthony anorak.

—We share the load, said Dad, packing everything away and heaving his pack on. I put mine on the floor, struggling into the straps and laying there like an upturned tortoise. Dad heaved me up with one hairy, aftershave-scented arm.

The hike was hellish.

—This is just the start, said Dad. Wait 'til we get to the real thing!

Within minutes, I'd dropped far behind, sullen about the books, shoulders aching, leather boots reeking of lanolin and biting my heels.

—This was supposed to be a holiday, I grumbled through tears.

I was terrible company, to my shame. Late in the afternoon, Dad gave up and we struck camp as the wind picked up and whistled through guide ropes. Still, he tried to jolly things along.

—Isn't this great? he kept roaring over the gale.

I glowered at him over my folding spoon, crunching on bits of undissolved mash.

The gale became much worse in the night, beating our tent with fists, then tearing at it with teeth. I could hear Dad cursing from where my head was buried deep in my sleeping bag. It was the night of the infamous Fastnet yacht-race disaster. As our tent came to pieces around us, a huge maritime rescue operation had unfolded off the coast of Ireland and eighteen people lost their lives.

We struggled out of the ruin of canvas early next day to collect the pots and food sachets spread over the mountain-side. On the way back down, it was Dad's turn to be sullen as I chattered happily and, when we eventually trudged back to the guest house, I retrieved my books.

We spent the next three days going to the cinema and eating at restaurants.

It was one of the best holidays I'd ever had.

We took the ferry home and hiked the last bit home from the bus with our heavy packs and clumping boots. At the garden gate, Dad stuffed the remains of our tent into the bin.

—The adventurers return, said my mother at door. I could hear our dog yapping out the back.

—I guess we were pretty lucky, said Dad. But that marked the end; our mountaineering days were over.

There would be no Kilimanjaro.

'Happy Berfday, Stoopid'

What exactly is the statute of limitations on burying one of your children's treasured art projects at the bottom of the dust bin?

I only stop to ponder this, fingers plucking at a frayed, stray, puke-green poster-painted *papier maché* strip on the broad-bean maraca I've just found wedged into a corner, because I'm trying to make space for my treasured rock music magazines.

At least, I'm assuming it's a maraca. I shake it. It rattles. I turn it over. *Dear Dab-dy* it says. Well, that dates it. I haven't been given a present by any of my kids in years. I turn it over again, edges stapled and trimmed, probably by a teacher. I give it a 'C' overall and chuck it into the 'toss' pile.

Digging deeper, I extract some sort of homemade greeting card from between a mildewed edition of *The Very Hungry Caterpillar* ('toss') and a lightly mauled Armadillo beanie toy ('not sure'—may be moderately collectable). The card's front shows the glued remnants of what may once have been spiral pasta. There's a cartoon figure as well, with sausage fingers and a balloon coming from its mouth. *Happy Berfday Stoopid* is what it says inside the balloon. I open the card, which sticks a bit. *Unly jocking*, it says inside, *iddiut*.

This, I decide, is a keeper. The other bits and bobs, the broad-bean maraca, an ancient toilet-paper-streamer tambourine, and the hideously floppy play-dough Nativity star left out to absorb the damp since Christmas God-knows-when, are now officially all doomed.

Most of these relics have been around for years. The stuff-space at the end of the long bookcase, slightly hidden by the bottom of the curtain, is a long forgotten last stop for school crafts, a limbo of crepe paper-stuffed hearts and grey, shapeless, crumbling sculptures.

Parents will know this place. It's a test. If it still has the power to tug on your heartstrings years later, it's a keeper (repack and repeat). If not, out it goes.

With four of our children having all snipped, stapled and glitter-bombed their way through entire childhoods of toilet roll re-purposing, our house would look one of those crazy person's places on TV, where the Council has to go in with biohazard suits to pry away some frazzled old timer's lifetime collection of prized empty microwave noodle pots, unless we had a system.

Specifically, I only keep stuff the kids have made that reinforces my fragile ego. *Luv you Dad* and *World Gratest Parunt* will do. *Happy Berthday Stoopid* and *Only jocking you iddiut* reinforces my delusion that I am in some way responsible for my children's kick-ass sense of humour.

—What are you doing? asks the fourteen-year-old

from somewhere behind raccoon eyes, wandering in and making me jump.

—I'm, um… I move the 'toss pile' slightly behind me with one foot.

—Oh wow, cool! She says diving on the pile. I remember this… She picks up the crumbling grey animal effigy with its stiff strands of pasta sticking out of its bum, which was soon destined to be reintroduced to the wild through the medium of bin lorry.

—Ah yes, I say. Who could forget the, uh… the…

—Horse, she says. What are you going to do with it? She pokes at one of its crumbling stumps.

—I was just giving that some serious consideration, I jabber, reddening.

—It could probably just go in the bin, she says reaching over to put it back.

—Ah, no way, I say, seizing it. I'd never…

—Can I have some money? she says, promptly losing interest.

—Ask your… but she bounces off on her toes before I'm finished… Mum.

I look at the thing in my hands. Another leg comes off in my fingers. *Looks like you've officially had it.* I chuck it back in the pile with a sigh.

When I've finally finished clearing out the corner and secreted a small bundle of items to the bin, I realise I've only actually gained about eight inches in shelf space, but it may be just enough for my treasured music magazines.

I go upstairs to get them from the newspaper rack in the bathroom but find only a few of the most recent copies. It takes a good five minutes crawling around the entire upstairs on all fours like a truffle pig before I locate the rest of the stack, squirrelled away behind an old basket of odd shoes, somewhere in a deep recess under our bed.

—You weren't going to throw those out, were you? I say, a little petulantly, when I find my wife.

—Oh, those? she says, with just the hint of a blush. I was just *storing* them there for a little while.

Glitter and Phallic Sheep

We don't do Christmas cards like we used to in our house. I want to add: 'like the old days', which conjures up images of top hats and wassailing, but it was only a few years ago that we'd sit down at the kitchen table and work through a stack of cards, rifling through a dog-eared address book for the street numbers of people we simply wouldn't contact by post for any other reason.

I remember that deep ache in the buffalo wing of flesh between thumb and forefinger after about the tenth card. I guess I haven't felt that in a while now. Writing anything but a scribbled initial on the electronic note pad belonging to an Amazon package delivery guy seems so strange now, like the wobbly spider feeling in your legs the first time you walk after being stuck in bed with a fever.

The first five Christmas cards we'd write would begin so neatly, with potted accounts of our year in the blank space opposite the printed greeting. *Dear... Can't believe it's Christmas again already…* By card number ten, it was *Have a good one…* In years when we'd exhaust our address books in the spirit of the season, we'd reach the point of a barely legible scribble.

—Can't we just sign the bloody things with an 'x', I'd say. Or a thumb print. It had nothing whatsoever to do with the quantity of Baileys consumed during the process.

At some stage, the cards didn't just slow to a trickle, they simply stopped. One Christmas, it seemed like we'd cards from all over the world wedged into every mirror in the house. The next, all we got was one Christmas card—from the postal service *An Post*.

—At least they signed it, I said, noting all the signatures inside. *Well, of course they did. Tens of thousands of cards they signed. By hand. Pillock.* My wife's expression said it all.

That was probably the year those declarations began appearing on Facebook and the like: W*on't be sending Christmas cards this year—instead, I'll be donating the money I'd usually spend, to help to buy a goat for a village in Mpumalanga…* Fair enough. There's no competing with a goat. But I had no idea that this was evidently an announcement on behalf of every last person we knew.

Still, we doggedly persisted in writing a gradually diminishing quantity of cards each Christmas, until one year we somehow neglected to even post the pile we'd written and found the sealed and addressed envelopes the following year at the bottom of a box of decorations.

No one seems to have been any the wiser. *Just check them for money and chuck them,* I suggested. It was clearly the end of an era.

When I was a kid, I loved nothing more than making my own Christmas cards. Give me a stack of coloured paper, some felt tipped pens, a bottle of that snotty glue with the runny rubber nose, and some glitter—and I was sorted for hours.

I considered myself a one-kid Christmas magic factory, humming high-pitched carols as I churned out personalized nativity scenes with stick-on foil stars. People loved my cards, I thought. Because who wouldn't love to open an envelope for an avalanche of glitter to embed itself in the good rug for the rest of the year?

Of course, I had no idea that my mother never even sent some of my best efforts. Years later, I found them in a scrapbook under her bed. There was the one of a nativity scene with some sort of farmyard animal, one can only hope, but in the shape of a giant set of male genitalia. Or the card that began, *Dear Grandma, sorry that you are old now and everybody you know is dead...*

The cards that were actually sent (who even knows) seemed somehow reciprocated and, as a child, I had a Pavlovian rush of butterflies at the metallic whine of our garden gate that signaled the arrival of the postman at Christmas; there would often be an envelope addressed just to me and stuffed with little strips of American candy or clippings from the bonkers *Weekly World News*.

That was my Aunt Donna. She'd stuff whatever she could into those Christmas envelopes, and the clippings only became stranger as she got older, like the one from that bonkers American tabloid about a B52 bomber being found on the moon, or even stranger, a coupon for a two-for one hot dog deal at some obscure American grocery store, on which she'd scribbled: *Wow!*

I'm sure it was revenge for years of glitter and phallic sheep, but I miss that lady terribly sometimes, particularly at Christmas.

One year, the postman rang the doorbell and asked for me, then gave me a very odd look as he handed over an envelope with a weird bulge in one corner from which seemed to be emanating a sort of miserable, wretched whining, like a tiny sheep giving birth. Tearing it open revealed a button on the card that said *Press here for Jingle Bells.*

It seems the pressure of the sealed envelope had activated the recording and for what was probably the duration of its 5,000 mile trip from California, this envelope had tortured its carriers with the incessant noise of a tinny electronic Christmas carol.

I'm not sure if that was the same year that America suffered a spate of post office worker gun rampages, prompting the phrase *gone postal*, but I can't help imagining, somewhere, Aunt Donna chuckling to herself.

Behind The Yellow Line

We gear up like warriors, but our body armour is thick coats with collars pulled high, one wing held in place against the wind with teeth. We're quilted and buttoned because the cold is like a jeering crowd, seeking every opportunity to reach out and wedgie you with a wolf whistle. But we are battened down and steeled. For we are *commuter*.

Bleep... Bleep... Bleep...

How do I find myself here again? Shuffling forward like a strange sort of paratrooper to the ticket screen. Return journey? We join the legion lining one edge of an iron ladder that seems to descend off into dark, Stygian depths, the city like lights of a thousand brooding bonfires somewhere distant.

The next train serves all stations to... Red letters blink and stutter.

We brace; black glass of our little shields at the ready, stuffing wires from them into our ears. Prepare to disengage.

Dismiss eye contact with a nod. It's how we always get through this: each to the bliss of our own tiny hell.

We move forward as one, but the growling, hissing beast that heaves our way is going the wrong direction and our shoulders sag.

It snakes in endlessly, groaning to a stop and disgorging the teeming contents of its bowels on the wrong side, our side, forcing us to break rank and peel away to let the day's survivors through, all pale faces, lit only by the glimmer of the hope of home. And then that dreaded thing: a familiar face that reaches out to clasp my elbow.

—Jaysus. It's yourself! says a voice.

I feel the cold pity of my fellow warriors as I'm forced to drop my mask and admit to who I am, a human with a life somewhere. They shift along, eyes buried deeper behind black glass shields, poking at the wires in their ears lest some overheard banality of the small-talk about to unfold wakes them too, and they also remember who they are.

—You look good, he lies.

—You do too, I lie also. He's ghostly white. Hasn't he been ill?

—Ticker, he says reading my mind

—Oh, I try, but I'm loathe to talk about such things as vulnerability. Not now, when I need to be who I need to be to get through an impending eight hour shift. Instead, I huff, shifting from foot to foot and beat my arms and squint over his shoulder at the glowing letters of the overhead display.

The next train serves all stations…

—In hospital… all kinds of tests, he says. I mean, I'm not that much older than *you*.

Anxiety slithers up my legs like black tendrils from the nearby Styx, cold as the gravel bed stretching off into winter dark beyond the single mocking eye of a signal light.

—Palpitations, so in I went to get it checked out. They kept me in...

In days of roaring diesel trains stained orange with filthy belching breath, my friends and I would shriek and gag as the engine thundered in, pushing past the walking dead with our army surplus school bags, whooping like lunatics as we stole light bulbs from the toilets, tugged down windows and smashed them on the tracks. We screamed at the tunnels. We were immortal.

—But I've already survived a lot of the men in my family, he says.

I can't get past *palpitation* and am already sinking backwards into a clammy hole where all I can think about is the Led Zeppelin drum solo my heart sometimes beats. No. My heart is a bad wedding drummer trying to force a reggae beat into the most inappropriate of songs, all crash-cymbal finale as the dancers stand around looking confused.

—Which you might want to get checked sometime, if you're worried at all, that is...

Am I a warrior or a worrier? Will I go gentle into the night cradling what could be a ticking time bomb in my chest like an old man clutching a bird? Or kick it ahead of me like an empty can, fearless of the din because I'd rather explode than creep into non-existence.

—And a stent is such a regular procedure nowadays, no worse than a root canal...

I'm seized by the irrational desire to leap into the dark and put my cheek to the cold metal below, purely to feel, smell and taste the freezing iron, the thrill of my mortality next to a hard and unforgiving surface.

Dad and I were on a walk when I was young and we

reached a level crossing. *Put your ear against the rail.* I did and heard a faint hum like the last note on a tuning fork. He fished out a two pence. *Put it on the track. When the train comes, it'll flatten it.* We stood back and clasped our ears when it finally hurtled past, but I never found the coin. It had vanished.

Please stand back behind the yellow line, train now approaching...

——Anyway, this looks like yours...

I turn to make polite apologies but find only the pale reflection I make in the station's closed doors now, eyes blinking back as the engine moans and wheezes in behind me.

We stumble on and find our seats, presenting shields, each settling in for quiet contemplation with respective gods, then heaving off toward the distant flickering lights, gathering speed until the hedgerows rush by like the waters of a fall.

Thaw

Whenever it snows, I think of the snowman I built with my older brother back in 1977.

I did all the work, getting up early, dressing up warm, and going out front to roll the huge snowballs I needed. I was super-excited. I'd never seen so much snow. I found an old pipe in the junk drawer and a carrot in the fridge: in no time at all I had a snowman.

Then my brother came out to help and ended up ruining everything, just like always.

—Look, he said. Now it has boobs.

I just stood there fuming, mittens hanging by elastic bands from my sleeves, face like thunder inside a furry hood.

—Fine, he said. Why didn't you tell me you hated boobs? and he took the snowman's head off with one punch.

Growing up, I never thought of my older brother as angry, or depressed, or mentally ill, I just thought of him

61

as a super pain in the ass. I don't think it's too strong to say that I hated him—not in the way a kid hates homework, or eating peas, those things can mostly be sat down, figured out and met head-on, or spirited away in a paper towel to the trash. No, I hated my older brother and I was pretty sure he hated me too.

I don't think he was even fourteen when he was expelled from school. Our parents sent him to a technical college after that, and then he ran away from home. I was just five, but I remember being in the back of the car while Dad drove around looking for him.

We stopped at a petrol station to ask the attendant, a teenager with scraggly hair and a bobbled hat, if he'd seen anything. Dad rolled down the window to talk to the guy but didn't like something he said, so he got out of the car. I don't remember hearing much more but the teenager's eyes got real wide. He dropped the nozzle he was holding, shook his head and pointed down the road.

We didn't find my brother. He was gone for perhaps a week, maybe more, or maybe it was just a few days. When he came back, he'd been smoking and drinking. There was shouting, then he went to his room and didn't come out for a long time.

He could sit for days just staring out his window. If you asked him what he was looking at, he'd say *nothin'*. Mostly, he wouldn't talk at all; he wouldn't even eat, just sit there. A huge dark cloud was over the whole house and all you could do was wait. Sometimes that cloud only dispersed when he left, slamming the door so loud the windows would rattle.

Dad brought him somewhere to get a whole bunch of tests done. I don't know what doctors looked for back then, but they didn't find anything. If they'd asked me, I'd have told them: *He's an idiot. He's no fun and I hate him.*

One time, he stabbed me in the eye with an umbrella and I had to go to hospital. I think he was sorry about that. I remember him looking at me, screaming *oh God, oh God, oh God.* Another time, he reached across the breakfast table when Mom was out of the room, picked up my toast and rubbed it all over my face. I yelled, but we both got in trouble, with him saying *you disgust me.*

When he was sixteen, I answered the front door and a Garda was standing there.

My brother ran out the back door, down the garden and disappeared over the wall, but it was just an outstanding parking ticket Dad had forgotten to pay. When my brother slunk back in, he didn't say a thing, and no one asked.

—Well, the good news is, you're a god damn genius, Dad told him, driving back from his hospital appointment That's all he said. He just kept chuckling and shaking his head, Heh-heh. A god-damn genius. My brother sat there, staring straight ahead.

Snow is made from almost nothing, only tiny crystals that super-freeze in the air and fall to earth, beautiful and treacherous. It could tickle you or bury you. You don't know which, and you don't ask. You can't stop snow and there's no point getting angry about it. Before you know it, it's gone, as if it was never there at all.

—Quit being such a girl, said my brother, bending over and scooping up handfuls. We both rebuilt the head, then found the pipe and carrot and stuck them in again too. I made two big balls of snow and slapped them on the snowman's chest.

—Boobs, I smiled, and maybe his face was just cold, but for a second, I thought my brother smiled too.

Next time my brother left, he never came back. I was in bed when he came to say goodbye.

—Guess you'd better give me a hug. I probably won't see you again for a long time, he said.

I thought it was a trick.

—No way, I said.

—Suit yourself, He shrugged and then he was gone.

Long after the last of the snow melted on the lawn, the snowman stayed, slowly melting to a pillar, then a tiny pile, until eventually there was nothing.

The day after my brother left, I dug out all the photo albums and searched through them until I found a picture of him: I put it in an old frame behind the lamp on my bedside table, where only I could see it.

For a couple of weeks, I stared at that picture every night, with a homesick feeling way down inside that was so bad, it made my throat hurt.

If my mother poked her head in to ask what I was doing, I wouldn't even look at her.

I'd just say *nothin'*.

What Men *Really* Talk About
on a Night Out

—*Chickens,* I whisper. Chickens running wild in the hedges and driving this bloke mad every morning, and he wants to know what we're going to do about it. I mean, do I look like the DSPCA?

My friend looks at me and cocks his head like he's considering this for a second.

—In the right light, he mocks, straightening his beer mat and chuckling. *Shesh-shesh-shesh!*

—Very funny, I mutter. Can you tell I don't get into the big city much these days?

—You're grand, says my friend. But, eh, just a hint. When someone says *How's things?* sometimes a simple *Fine, thanks,* will do the job. He shows me his palms. Just sayin'.

—Was I ranting? I say by way of apology.

—Only since you sat down, he says.

The girl behind the bar comes over.

—You look like you're in a world of your own, she says, wiping the counter.

—He's in an entire *universe* of his own, my friend smiles. He stretches the *u* in *universe* in a Dublin way that emphasises the point, but the girl says nothing, just turns around and begins slicing limes.

—Impervious to my charms, jokes my friend under his breath.

We're actually on a sort of pilgrimage tonight, my friend and I, to see a band from Portland called The Delines. The guitarist and songwriter, Willy Vlautin, is also one of our favourite authors.

It promises to be a sultry, atmospheric affair as the singer, Amy Boon, croons about troubled brothers, empty parking lots and the distant lights of lonely oil rigs.

—Any singer, says my friend, who used to sing in a band called The Damnations, is fine by me.

—We should go, I tell him. Thanks, I call to the girl behind the bar. She turns her head and holds up a wedge of lime, mouthing a cheers in response.

We step out onto the street.

—How's the missus? asks my friend.

—Fine, thanks, I glare at him jokingly. Actually, I confess as we trudge towards traffic lights, the chicken story was hers.

—Well, she *certainly* doesn't look like the DSPCA. *Shesh*! he chuckles.

—Careful now, I tell him.

I watch the lights of the crossing count down.

—You should say to her, says my friend, eyes twinkling, next time someone comes in about a chicken problem, she should tell them exactly what they should do about it.

I wait for it.

—One hundred and eighty degrees for two hours, he says. Few slices of pineapple. Rice on the side. Your only man.

—What would we do without you.

We cross over and make our way up the long street towards the venue.

—Would she not come in tonight herself? he says.

—I think she just sort of thought she'd leave us to it, I tell him.

—If only women knew, he says, launching into full performance mode again, what men talk about when we're 'left to it'. Sex? Violent films? No, chickens and Americana bands."

—And cooking, I remind him.

—And *kewkin'*, he says. *Shesh!*

I'm supposed to meet up with more old friends at a pub but I'm suddenly confused by the street. I stop and look around, then ask someone at a bus stop for directions.

—*Pfft*, says my friend disbelievingly. You don't know where Whelan's is?

—Straight ahead, says the man at the bus stop. Two sets of traffic lights. It's on the right.

—Jaysus, Dave, says my friend, covering his face.

—You know, I tell him, trudging on. We were staying in the city on a sort of romantic break one night and we suddenly noticed we were walking right behind you. You were going the same way we were and we had to follow you for ages.

I'd always felt a little guilty about that. My wife and I had selfishly kept our distance, not wanting to get into a conversation, wanting to keep the night to ourselves.

—At one point we stood right beside you at a traffic light. I think you had your earphones in.

—How do you know, he says, looking at **me sidelong,** that I didn't know you were there. Maybe *I* **didn't want to** talk to *you.*

—Right. You got me, I smile, shaking my **head.**

We finally reach the pub, with just enough **time to get a** pint before the gig. My friend's nephew is **there too. He's** already met the band and had albums signed. **The apple** doesn't fall far from the family tree.

When the band comes on stage, I find a **spot near the** front and tip Willy Vlautin a wink as he **steps up to the microphone.**

—This set goes out to our friend George **tonight, he** says, wherever he is.

I look at the empty space in the crowd bes**ide me where** my friend should be.

—He's right here, I hear myself say.

He wouldn't miss this for the world.

Then the music starts, the crowd moves for**ward and the** space beside me is gone.

John 'George' Byrne, Herald Critic, April 2, 2015. RIP

Spike Says Hello

It's a long January taxi ride home through late, lamp-lit streets, fleeting images out of a rain-speckled rear passenger window making a Victorian zoetrope of staggering ghosts, tumbling trash and torn posters in the flitting shadows between pools of light.

My driver lets the sticky floor-tom drum solo of rubber wheels on wet stone cobbles finish before asking: *Bridge or tunnel?*

—Bridge, I tell him, and before long the black Liffey is gleaming with the carnival lights of dockland office buildings.

—Changed, hasn't it? he says.

I'd been hoping not to have to talk so soon into the thirty-minute journey.

—It has, I manage.

—Do y'remember the Dandelion Market? he says. It's a test. Your answer says how old you are.

—I bought my first badge there, I tell him.

Boomtown Rats. I only had it ten minutes when some gouger tried to grab it. He chased me through Fiddlers Green where I tried to lose him in the crowd, but he caught up, took the badge and gave me a punch in the head. *Posh bastard* he hissed and spat on my shoes. I'd never seen anything like it, this kid with his shaved head, boots and snarls. It was my first time in the city and my first unceremonious introduction to what was the early 1980s culture of Dublin tribes.

—Rats? says the driver. How old are yeh, fifties? He looks in the rear view mirror and I nod. Same as meself, he says and I can't help wondering for a moment if he ever chased a posh kid down for his badge.

—I had me hair in a Mohawk, he continues, which solves that mystery. The girls loved Mohawks, but I was always more into Skin culture than Punk.

The ability to place someone in the tribal spectrum in that era was second nature. Punk had any number of spin-offs, Nazi Punks, Jah Punks, punks identified by particular bands, Sex Pistols punks who always seemed to have a bit of a loose screw, or Damned punks that blurred the line between Punk and Goth.

If you were into The Undertones and SLF, you might be considered *Soft Punk*. Those with badges of bands like Crass were considered *Hard Punk*. Anyone into bands like Exploited were considered a bit of a joke, as were *shop bought* Punks with expensive tartan trousers and jackets purchased by parents at places like No Romance on Aungier Street.

There were 'good Skins' and 'bad Skins'—the clue was in the badges again, or by the colour of their boot laces, or whether they wore Harringtons or bomber jackets, and whether the bomber jackets were green or black.

'Good Skins' were into Ska and Reggae, they were anti-Nazi Punk and wore badges with Stiff and Two Tone record label logos side by side, and they never wore white or red boot laces, which were generally considered to have racist associations.

The skinheads that were feared and loathed wore black bomber jackets and tight, bleach-mottled jeans tucked inside black, 18-hole Doc Martins with white laces. If you saw some of them coming, you crossed the street and made yourself scarce.

There were Goths and New Romantics and Cureheads who didn't particularly associate with either but looked a little like both, and there were a few Teds that looked like skinheads with quiffs, and Psychobillies who really were skinheads with quiffs.

I was a Rude Boy, into bands like The Specials and The Selecter, in a black Harrington with SKA printed on the back in white letters: then I moved into Jah Punk, which to me just meant you dressed like a punk but still bought reggae and Ska records.

Exit signs for the airport are sliding by now, bright in the sudden headlights, then disappearing in the dark, like memories.

—I was never really into the violence, says the taxi driver. Plenty were, I wasn't.

He started playing drums, he says, in bands supporting the likes of Paranoid Visions in places like the Ivy Rooms, names that make my head reel with nostalgia.

Ska heads and punks sitting together in front of the local shopping centre in days of cranky bus conductors, tea shops and stinking phone booths. Cigarettes and seven-inch singles from the change you robbed from your mother's purse. Your nickname in black marker on every street-light pole. Your horrified mother: *Where were you? Out. Out where? Just out.* Posters of The Clash on bedroom walls.

I tell him where I used to hang out, gangs of punks stomping around gorse hills above our suburb, torn trousers, home-made studded belts, band T-shirts and old granddad coats. Spitting, breaking bottles and spray painting band names on concrete walls.

Some of them are still in bands, I say. But it all seems like another life now, those days of Dublin tribes, and what might have seemed a whole lifetime was probably just a teenage year, but I'm still in touch with one or two of them, and I rattle off nicknames.

The taxi driver recognises one of the names as well as the band he's in now, four decades after they hung around St Stephen's Green, back when none of us planned to ever grow up, or get jobs, or meet other punks with grey hairs, in a taxi.

We pull up in the dark outside my house.

—If you're talkin' to him, he says, tell him Spike said hello.

George Lucas How Are Ya?

At somewhere around number three on my top 10 list of bizarre occupations that I have pursued with people who in any other era would probably have been trussed up and flung gibbering into a padded cell (journalism being number one on that list) is that of television camera operator.

It was the mid-1990s and the TV station was Marin Channel 31, situated minutes north of San Francisco's Golden Gate Bridge, just past San Quentin State Prison which housed the world's largest population of death row inmates, and spitting distance from Lucas Film's San Rafael headquarters.

That these things coexisted in such relative proximity seemed anything but strange in this series of tiny towns stumbling distance from one another, where you were as likely to meet Robin Williams as Tupac Shakur, hippy icon Wavy Gravy, or Sean Penn in your local grocery store.

I worked in a printing plant at night, where we designed and printed collectible Elvis phone cards, a plant owned by future Google vice president Larry Brilliant, and where Robin Williams once strolled through, shy and soft spoken, on a shop floor tour and no one batted an eyelid.

By day, however, I was chief intern at Marin 31, a position which mostly involved me time-logging show tapes and fast forwarding through hours of bonkers public access program submissions to search for full frontal nudity, which was just about the only thing that was against the rules to air.

Marin County was an epicenter of film tech, with Lucas Film, Skywalker Ranch and THX all nearby. They had recently set up camp next door to work on special effects, notably a mysterious, foot-high, mile long tunnel through which a tiny, rocket-propelled vehicle was fired along rails all day long.

I'd taken to wearing movie industry T-shirts and caps and once got a free meal at the local Mexican restaurant because they mistook me for a Lucas Film crew member. *Are you with the lunch party of Mr Lucas?* said the checkout lady. *Does it show?* I lied.

It was the best taco I'd ever eaten.

That was about as exciting as it got in an environment where strange was routine, yet I was quite full of myself when I was promoted to trainee camera operator at the channel. *Next stop,* I'd mutter to myself as I gazed longingly over at the enshrouded campus belonging to the *Star Wars* creator.

Unfortunately, it wasn't so simple. We were a cable network with a busy public access channel; being behind a camera on the studio floor meant a welcome break from sifting through the amateur drivel that arrived on tape by the bag load, but I still had to deal with nutters.

It was about as far away from Lucas Film as a dive-bar grill slab is from Nouvelle cuisine.

One of the first shows I worked on turned out to be a long-running late-night studio series on Tantric sex, in which a 400-pound Samoan gentleman huffed his way through seemingly unlimited breathing techniques for prolonging orgasm. My job was to keep my camera on the sign-language interpreter.

There was a transvestite panel show that was about as dull as Mass, without the wine and crackers, and there was an hour-long, one-man rant show on conspiracies that routinely needed so much staff editing by the end— due to the fact that it focussed almost entirely on local government, and featured photos of male genitalia—it only ran to about twelve minutes on air.

There was a show titled *Mysterious Animals*, or something similar, in which the host presented footage, 'indisputable proof' of the existence of, variously over consecutive weeks, a yeti, a spider the size of a small dog, and a giant boar, all in nearby Tamalpais woods. Giant *bore* was more like it.

His footage invariably consisted of shaky point-of-view angles speeding between bushes close to the ground, as though his mysterious creatures were carrying the camera. Completely bats.

Almost ten years before YouTube existed, every fruitcake with a half-baked idea for a TV show was taking advantage of their right to do so at their local cable public access station; the most lunatic of them all were right here in California.

But then, if Marin County native George Lucas had submitted a proposal to Marin Channel 31 for his very first film idea, *THX 1138*, in which a populace is controlled by androids that prescribe mandatory drugs to suppress sexual desire, he might have fitted right in with the programme schedule.

With a studio full of expensive equipment at my disposal, I took to shooting and editing my own short shows that attempted to satirize crazy public access television, under the moniker *The Lazy Drunk Hour*.

I aired a potted philosophy show filmed under the stall door of a men's toilet; the pilot for a dating comedy about a violent zoo-ape named Brian, and a chat show featuring a cigar-smoking host in a Mexican wrestler's mask interviewing an Argentinian midget named Peanut Del Ray.

There was no competing, however. When the thing you're trying to make fun of is already so utterly demented that anything you can possibly offer pales in comparison, it's time to back away. I backed away so far I ended up all the way back in Ireland, no doubt leaving behind a creative void that allowed Lucas to focus on his next *Star Wars* film, *The Phantom Menace*—though judging by Jar-Jar Binks, he may still have been tuning in to public access television just a little too much.

Me, I haven't picked up a camera since, but there are some Lazy Drunk Productions still floating around out there—where it belongs, on YouTube, with all the other deranged nonsense.

Pranked by Father Stone

A million years ago, before my wife and I were married, we decided to move into a flat together for the first time and we chose to live in the very first one we went to see.

We might have looked at three flats and found two that were nicer than the basement of a gloomy Georgian house in Monkstown, but then we'd never have ended up living downstairs from a character from *Father Ted*.

Come to think of it, our new landlady's name was Mrs Doyle and there was more than a touch of Craggy Island about her, but we wouldn't have known that at the time because *Father Ted* was still a few years off.

And yet, Michael Redmond was already every bit of Father Stone, the only difference being that Michael was the sort of company you very much wanted, whereas *Father Ted*'s Paul Stone would be famously stultifying.

I can't remember how we became aware of each other. There was an old rotary dial payphone in the hall;

sometimes it rang and rang until someone bothered to answer it and had to go off knocking on doors.

Whether he answered the door to me, or I to him, I immediately liked the droopy-moustached face that greeted me. Michael had perfected the sort of eyes which should been in an encyclopaedia under the word 'dead-pan'.

He could say the most innocuous thing, we soon found out, and make it gut-wrenchingly funny because he'd never crack a smile, he'd just look at you with that face like a Dali painting melting over a stick.

Already well known as a comic on the London scene, he had a bit in his routine about going shopping - for a Mars bar—that ended with him breaking the news to the shopkeeper that he was 'just browsing'. Only Michael could tell that story and look utterly baffled when you laughed. And the more baffled Michael looked, the funnier it was.

Soon after moving in, we ended up fellow insomniacs; I'd shuffle upstairs, knock quietly so as not to wake his girlfriend, and we'd sit together in front of the fire and not talk, just me and one hundred per cent Father Stone.

Arthur Matthews and Graham Linehan mightn't have even started the script, but hands down, Michael Redmond already had the character of Father Stone to a tee.

As we got to know one another, we'd occasionally double date, once going together with our girlfriends and ending up, of all places, at the nearby *Comhaltas* Irish Culture Centre, for the late night *seisiun*.

I'd be surprised now if the entire night hadn't been engineered by Michael, that I somehow ended up there with the goatskin *bodhran* drum my girlfriend had given to me.

Was it Michael who gave her the idea to give me the **drum? Was** it not him that plied me with pints and got me **to join in** with some of the groups? *They love the bodhran, he said,* straight-faced, with his serious moustache. *No, really. They do.*

I'm pretty sure, every time I looked up, bleary eyed from **the midst** of whatever poor musicians I'd foisted myself **on, beati**ng away on my goatskin, Michael was looking **back, hang**dog serious, all encouraging thumbs.

Days later, the night all but a fuzzy memory, I received **a letter w**ith a perfectly imperfect logo bearing the legend **'Friends o**f the Bodhran'. *Pleasure to meet the other night,* it **read. *Plea**se come to one of our meetings and share with us.*

The only thing missing was a sign off with *you will, you will, you will…* but God love me, I was delighted and off **I went, c**lutching my bodhrán in one hand, my letter in **the other.**

Not even when some poor old fella with one arm **missing** wrestled the door open, took one look at my **bodhrán** before promptly slamming the door in my face, **did I reco**gnise the work of a master joker.

It was only as I trudged back up the path to our house, **bedraggl**ed with rain, and noticed Michael's girlfriend **in the w**indow, collapsing with laughter, that I had an **inkling.** I knocked on his door. He answered, stony-faced. **I held up** the letter.

—**You** didn't by any chance, I began, but all six foot six **of Micha**el had doubled over. It was the first time I'd ever **seen him** crack.

—**You** didn't actually *go?* Michael finally managed **through** tears.

I did, I told him. The man with only one arm had been **a nice to**uch, I said. Friends of the Bodhrán, indeed.

—Only… one… arm? Michael's stony face creased into fits again. Turned out he'd picked the address at random from the directory dangling from the phone in the hall. He never thought I'd go and certainly hadn't a clue who actually lived there, or that they'd only one arm.

I let Michael believe that I forgave him. He moved back to London and was soon special guest on Series One, Episode Two of *Father Ted*, the now infamously titled 'Entertaining Father Stone'—and the rest is sitcom history.

Somewhere along the line, we reconnected after Michael moved to Edinburgh, where his one-man show titled 'I Wrote a Joke in 1987' was part of the Fringe Festival. When the show previewed at Dublin's Smock Alley, I mentioned in an article that I had paid for an entire bus load of bodhran players to keep him company when he went on stage.

Or had I? I decided I'd just let him sweat about that.

Old Jim Died of Gut Gas

The last time I remember the grass dying was 1976. Summer lasted forever; at age nine it took years to plod to the beach with togs tucked into the Swiss-roll of a towel under your arm, forever to wince into the water past your waist, and a lifetime for your turn in the queue for a dripping cone at the ice cream van.

I didn't think our family was weird. Dad was a writer and a jazz musician who jobbed as a sub editor on the national daily. In his spare time he brewed beer and took us to cemeteries where he made crayon rubbings of tombstones while we were sent looking for the grave of the washerwoman from whom his 'spirit guide' had told he was reincarnated.

Just like any Dad, really.

Dead summer heat summons it all: the smell of his simmering hops in the kitchen; the crackle of my mother's transistor radio in the garden as she sieved the earth around the roses with her fingers between deep drags on her cigarette; the *rat-a-tat-tat* of Dad's typewriter through the ceiling; the scream of a neighbour as her daughter was launched into the air by a speeding vehicle.

That's how I remember 1976.

I secretly shuffled through Dad's papers, reading through the scrawl of his 'automatic writing'; this is where he wrote—his hand moved, he said, by a spirit named Michael—that I too had been a woman in another life, married to a rock climber who had been killed in a fall.

Just your average family.

At night Dad would sometimes have a Dutch man over named Pete who played trumpet. The two would jam together while Pete's wife and my mother made small talk over gins. Eventually the music would be drowned out by the incessant alarm-bell ring of the telephone, signalling the neighbours' distaste. Once they called to the door as Dad and his friend pounded out some jazz number.

Some days Dad would drag us off in our tiny, ancient, belching Hillman, to Wicklow, which took several lifetimes. If my mother was annoyed, which she often was on these trips, she would stare out the passenger side window for the whole way. "Whatever," or "I don't care," is all she'd say. I would lay my head on the hot vinyl of the back seat and hum along to the changing of gears.

We brought a little butane camp stove and fried sausages in a pan at Devil's Glen, because you couldn't get hot dogs in 1976. We'd dab them with English mustard, because it's the only mustard I remember, and wrap them in bread. Dad would flick open a vast black umbrella to try and ward off the flies, but it only amplified the sound of the swarms until we'd finally give up and leave.

A woman named Betina stayed with us that summer,

from something called 'the Inner Peace Movement'. She taught us how to read each others' auras.

If you stared at someone long enough while they stood in front of a white surface, you'd begin to see the colours, she said. Betina was on the Late Late Show, but it didn't feel strange at all to have someone famous in our house.

Dad showed Betina his 'automatic writing'. "I start with a scribble and then it just comes," he told her. She asked if he'd ever tried using his typewriter to contact the spirit world. Just once, he said. Rat-a-tat-tat. He pulled the paper from the roller and the words stamped on the paper said: *Old Jim died of gut gas.* He said he never tried again. I'm not sure why that story scared me so much.

I moved through these conversations like a tourist viewing the rooms of an exhibit. Outside, summer grilled the potted plants to a crisp. Dad's beer soured in the barrel, making the whole front hall smell like vinegar and grass clippings. The heat of the sun seemed to have its own sound.

In the middle of the tarmac on the road outside, I found the two tiny front teeth of the girl next door.

The first time I heard the word 'drought' was in 1976. The news that crackled on the radio kept talking about bomb attacks in the North. I couldn't get the song *Save All Your Kisses for Me* by the Brotherhood of Man out of my head, even though I hated it. I was humming it to myself when my mother jumped out from behind a door with her fake tooth sticking out of her mouth on its wire. *Bahhhh!* she shouted, then laughed until she cried. I hated when she did that. Once, she picked up a pair of scissors and said *I just want to fix your lips.* I locked myself in the bathroom, even though I knew she was joking.

I never longed for normal parents. I'm not sure I knew

what the word meant. Once, I was sent to bed early because they thought the film on TV was going to be too scary and it was past my bedtime. I shouted down the stairs: *When I grow up, I'm never going to be as boring as you!*

I wonder whatever happened to that beaten-up old Hillman, or if anyone ever inherited a huge old black umbrella that is terrible for fending off flies.

The lawn behind our old house is probably as brown now as it was in 1976, the hand-sieved soil dry in the rose beds nearby, where I planted two tiny teeth.

I don't believe in auras, vibrations, or other lives, but a long, dry summer still smells of simmering hops to me. It crackles like an old radio and buzzes like flies around hot mustard. Just like 1976.

Best Stripper in Town

Hunger is a great motivator. It's amazing what a person will do for food, or for the money to buy some—and quickly. I've been there and I didn't have to miss many meals before I fell to stripping.

Yes, stripping. I don't mean stripping the paint off houses, either, or stripping cars in a wrecker's yard for parts. Those jobs implied a level of skill and patience that I simply could not imagine at the tender age of twenty. This was a whole different level.

Put it this way, if jobs like house-painting or panel beating were up around the tenth floor in the pantheon of potential paying occupations, I'd discovered a hidden manhole somewhere in the basement that led to a subterranean cavern so deep that I would soon be breaking into a sweat from the heat through the walls because of its sheer proximity to Hell. Even half-naked.

—You're hired, is the way the guy answered the phone

when I called the number on the flyer. We'll try you out tonight.

I was to meet a black van in a city centre alleyway at 9pm. Nothing dodgy about that, right? This was the routine. Meet the van, jump in the back, change into the outfit supplied…

—You're serious, right? I choked when I saw it.

—Don't forget the boxers, the driver called over a shoulder as the van clattered over ramps, throwing me around like some sort of disappointing novelty rag doll. He lobbed a balled-up pair of bright pink boxer shorts with a teddy bear pattern print. I winced.

I yelled over the screaming engine as we raced along.

—So, are you my bodyguard when we get there, too?

The words came out a little too high pitched, like a choir boy.

—Yeh wha'? coughed the driver, laughing so hard between convulsive hacking, he had to wipe his eyes with his sleeves as he wrestled the wheel, almost setting his hair alight with the glowing butt of his cigarette.

—Sorry lad, he finally managed, shaking his head. You're on your own.

The van pulled up at a redbrick terrace, hitting the curb hard. I hauled the heavy door aside and clambered out, trying to regain my land-legs and get my bearings. A few yards away, a single gold balloon bobbed from a gate.

Steeling myself, I adjusted my collar and was about to go for it when the gruff voice came again.

—Forget something?

I snatched the battered cassette player from a hairy arm, then trotted up the path.

As I rang the doorbell, I could see the shadows of party-goers through frosted glass.

—What the hell am I doing? I muttered as one shadow peered back and the door shuddered open, revealing a woman in her seventies.

—Father, she smiled. So glad you could make it.

There are moments when the threads of one's life suddenly draw neatly together and the path ahead is revealed in crystal clarity. There are others when one's stomach drops through the floor of one's abdomen as though one has been dropped from a great height and is now free-falling into a gaping abyss.

I was ushered into the hubbub of a busy drawing room, clawing at the air as my cassette player was whisked off to a sideboard and replaced with a cup and saucer of tea. The Velcro tabs of my quick-release costume trousers rubbed against bare skin, already stinging with sweat. I tugged at my clerical collar.

—Sandwich? said someone. I didn't need to be asked twice and began fisting triangles of coronation chicken into my famished face.

—He looks very young to be a priest, observed someone.

—Mmmph-phoober, I explained through hamster cheeks.

—Ohhh, he's a student priest, translated someone else.

Two short, irritated beeps sounded from the van as more people milled in, someone now handing around a tray of Mr Kipling cakes. It was now or never. Gulping down my last golf-ball of sandwich, I leapt onto the chair, jabbed the 'play' button on the cassette player and ripped my trousers off in one sweeping gesture, bucking my hips to the bawdy trombone of something like *Roll Out the Barrel*.

—Haaa-py anni-vers-reee, I sang, just liked I'd learnt. Hap-py anny-vers-ree Mam and Daaaad. I swung my jacket through the air and yanked off the clerical collar. The rest of the verse is a blur, but there were personal details, something about Mam liking to play Bridge and Dad being a pigeon fancier. I don't think any of it even rhymed.

Darting between frozen statues back towards the door, I grabbed the tape player and discarded clothes, nabbing a handful of French Fancies on the way, before diving back into the van, which screeched off in a plume of exhaust.

Looking back, I can't even be sure we had the right house, but I got fed, paid twenty quid and dropped back to where I'd been picked up.

—Same time tomarra'? growled the driver. I looked guiltily from side to side and shuffled my feet.

—S'pose, I said.

Alas, my career as a stripping vicar with Sam's Singing Telegrams was short lived, even though I'm pretty sure I showed promise. Before too long, despite a string of gigs, I began getting published enough to feed myself, but it was nice to know I had something to fall back on.

I kept the ridiculous pink boxer shorts, just in case.

Captain Lou's

I'm guessing that, like me, a lot of people have a happy place they sometimes visit in their heads. Those with religion console themselves with prayer. Smart people might do puzzles in their heads. Some meditate, slipping into the saline embrace of their minds' ocean. Others just hum a tune. Me, I go to Captain Lou's.

I discovered Captain Lou's on a trip to the States to see my Mom in the small, lakeside town where she lived. South Haven is hometown USA, all barbecues, deck chairs and lawn sprinklers. American flags adorn the front of wooden houses and summer nights light up with fireflies. It truly is the land of blueberry pie and homecoming queens: some people never leave.

I'd try to find the time to poke around the quiet little stores on the short main street. One place sold giant cookies; another had wind chimes and hanging spinners; there was a shop full of scented soaps and candles. There was also a diner, a doughnut shop, the old movie theatre and a Dairy Queen.

Ducking from awning to awning to avoid the heat of the early afternoon sun, it's about as far from a busy, damp Dublin day as you can imagine and, from here, Captain Lou's is only a few minutes away.

You cross the street between huge pick-up trucks parked nose to curb, and head down a side street, nodding to an old man in shorts, sneakers and a Cubs baseball hat balanced on his head. You pass the faded glory of the movie theater, with its Fifties Deco facade, then find the river at the end of the street and follow it up to the blue bridge.

As you get nearer, you see flashing red lights signal traffic to stop while the bridge yawns to let a puttering sail boat through. Seagulls wheel and cry. A couple of Harley's idle, then rev as the bridge closes over. You hope they're not stopping at Captain Lou's, a favourite biker haunt, but they roar off toward South Beach.

Crossing the bridge on the narrow cement walkway, a passing car makes the warm, hollow thrum of rubber on steel grill as you note the familiar pink neon cursive sign on the shack tucked away below the far side of the bridge. It's open. It look like you have the whole place to yourself, deck and all. You smack your lips. You're thirsty now and could kill a bottle of beer.

You take the steps down to the bar two at a time, stopping only to breathe in and savour the warm sunshine, the river smell, before pushing open the door.

The walls inside are not cluttered, just a few mirrors with beer logos: Michelob, Bud Light—no-nonsense, working-men's beer. The ceiling flutters with banknotes, a lot of them dollar bills with messages scrawled on them. There's a sign on the bar advertising Fireball shots, and a pleasant smell lingers as though something has been freshly fried. A baseball game crackles on a tiny radio.

The barman pokes his head in from the deck, chewing. He licks his fingers and smiles, wiping his hands on a bar towel. He's wearing shorts and a bright summer T-shirt that says 'Bahama Mama'.

—Hey there, he says. Canna getcha.

—Red Stripe, you say without hesitation. He nods, still smiling and fishes a fat, brown bottle from a trough of half-melted ice. He puts the bottle on the counter, digging in his short apron for the opener as you watch one of the drops of condensation on the neck of the bottle burst into a rivulet and run down the label. He pops the cap with a flourish, lifts the bottle and puts it down a little closer to you.

You take a long swig from the bottle, ignoring the slight brain freeze and the ache in your throat from the fizz, only stopping to take a breath and belch into your fist, raising an eyebrow in apology, wiping your mouth on the sleeve of your shirt.

—Getcha summin a eat? says the barman. Got fresh perch, fished a s'mornin'.

You consider this.

—Mmm, thought I might just have a burger.

—Everything on? He finds a patty and turns on his heels to slap it sizzling onto the nearby griddle.

—One Lou, comin' up, he says. Now… how 'bout another Stripe?

You fill your lungs with the delicious mist of frying beef and look from your bar stool to where the sun dapples the surface of the river a couple of yards away; it's then that you catch yourself… happy.

Captain Lou, see, is a state of mind. That power-pop song on a bright Sunday morning as you crack a couple of eggs into a pan, that's Captain Lou too, as is that moment when the evening holds its breath between sundown and dark and birdsong carries for miles, or the feel of the fur of your dog on your feet beneath the table when you sit down to a perfect meal. That's Captain Lou.

I don't know if I'll ever be back to the real Captain Lou's again. I don't know if I want to—or even need to.

All I need is to be able to summon up the picture of that barman scooping up a second beer and stacking cheese and grilled onions on top of a sizzling disc of meat nearby.

Or to catch myself happy.

Give Them Hell

If anyone were to ask about the worst job I've had, I might consider that bar in the sticks where I struggled to understand a word the punters said, until the day I fell through a plate-glass window after being sent up on the roof to dispose of a disemboweled rabbit someone had lobbed there.

But as jobs go, lasting facial scars aside, it wasn't a bad one for a sixteen year old. We were paid cash and got a free pint at the end of every day, plus bed and board. Sure, six weeks of it were spent on a hospital drip, but the boss did replace the T-shirt that had been ripped open as they attempted to revive me.

In the bad old 1980s, you pretty much took any job for whatever money was going, and a succession of these saw me grinding bad meat and blood into sausages, then working in kitchens among heat-crazed chefs who shattered plates against walls as a means of expression.

But the weirdest job I ever had, one that I am only

comfortable recalling now that the major players are either dead or have changed their names, was for a travelling theatre company, performing two shows daily for a year, often under threat of physical violence or prematurely exploding effects.

I've worked for all manner of pirates and cut-throats in the intervening decades before I found my way to the comparative calm of a computer keyboard, but not one has ever hissed through clenched teeth, *get out there and make them scream or I will kick the living shit out of you.*

In fairness, on that occasion, our lead actor had just knocked out her two front teeth on a colleague's head during the infamous 'King of the Devils' scene, where a wizard summoned forth a rubber and latex horror amid exploding pyro-flashes, as the first two rows of infants fled shrieking from the assembly hall.

But this was life on the road for seven of us packed into the back of a speeding Hi-Ace van, careening around the back roads of Ireland, surrounded by teetering crates of dodgy electronic pyrotechnics. And while I hesitate to use the word 'hell, our performances were frequently tinged with the odour of singed eyebrows after a small on-stage explosion was triggered by some faulty connection.

Our mission, spat from behind the shuddering steering wheel as the van thundered into some unsuspecting playground, was to give the schoolchildren a performance unlike anything they'd ever seen, or were ever likely to see again. *Make them wee*, was the director's agenda.

It all started with a notice for an audition on a bulletin board in what was then the Centre for the Performing Arts on Ormond Quay, where it wasn't unusual to bump into Liam Neeson smouldering over a cup of bad coffee. I'd been rehearsing *Philadelphia Here I Come* upstairs with a young actor named Aidan Murphy, until we disbanded due to lack of interest (someone, somewhere would someday be kicking themselves after Aidan changed his surname to Gillen).

Despondent, I slipped into the audition and found myself landing a lead role in a children's play that was due to tour primary schools. It wasn't much, but it was paid work and rehearsals were to begin immediately, in the basement of was known, rather aptly perhaps, as *The Black Church*.

Underfunded and under-rehearsed, we hit the road in a dirty big van, retrofitted to carry seven actors, a full set, lighting rig, sound equipment and, key to the whole thing, hundreds of pounds of electronically triggered pyro-flash boxes, or, effectively, one hell of a lot of gunpowder.

The first two or three thousand children, 150 per school, twice a day, five days a week, passed largely without incident or injury, other than the seething contempt with which our director-turned-van driver and effects supervisor 'motivated' us. Indeed, we may even have been entertaining.

It was only as actors and equipment began to fray that things deteriorated. Sets would collapse in the middle of key scenes, or an explosion would go off at the wrong time, temporarily blinding an actor and sending them flailing into the children.

Once, there was even a fistfight between the director and an actor behind the curtain that spilled onto the stage as a hundred children and their teachers looked on in awe, wondering if it was all part of the show. In many ways, increasingly, it was.

Finally, things quite literally came to a head the day our lead actor knocked her teeth out in the middle of a scene. While she was being carted off to the doctor, the show went on, with us rewriting the wretched thing on the fly, under threats from behind the curtain of a hiding otherwise.

When the entire troupe conspired to break our contracts and go our separate ways, we were told we'd never work again and, well, most of us were quite happy not to, in children's theatre at least.

The Fine Art of Disappearing

Someone asked me recently, where do you go to reset? How do you recharge? The man who asked me this is a relatively new convert to sea swimming and hasn't missed a day in the Irish Sea in seven months, sunshine, sleet or gale. He says that the act of plunging himself into water that is preferably near freezing, prompting the body to go into emergency mode as early onset hypothermia sets in, blood rushing to vital organs, including the brain, produces a rush of endorphins. He says this never fails to exhilarate, to recharge his batteries, to give him a fresh perspective on things.

Different strokes, right? I have a rather more ignominious relationship with the Irish winter sea plunge. At Dublin's famous Forty Foot, at age ten, I stood shivering on the brink in tiny togs with my friend and his father.

—Go on, said the dad. Go on, for Christ's sake.

He gave me one hard shove and in I went.

To me the cold was a white wall of pain, so cold that it burned. A comic turn of phrase comes to mind: *Jesus walked on water, Diebold did the fifty meter sprint.* In fact, I clawed my way out of the water and onto a rock, gasping and retching. My ears hummed and my head rang. Someone came over to check on me.

—Oh he's fine, said my friend's dad, his face a mask of disdain. You're fine.

I tried it again just a few years ago at Christmas. Shuffling into the numbing water to cheers, I stood there grinning and rubbing my hands until the cheers turned to jeers and everyone eventually drifted away. One little red-headed kid remained. He tossed a small stone into the water beside me. *Chicken*, he said, then turned and left. When I made the plunge, no one saw.

How do I reset, recharge, get a new perspective? Well, near-freezing water doesn't do it, evidently. Neither does the idea of any painfully clichéd so-called life-affirming bucket list experience. Feel free to jump off the bridge with your ankles in a sling. I'll mind your beer. Parachuting? Knock yourself out. No, please, do. Anything worthy of a selfie, for me, is powerless to reset or reaffirm.

One person's elixir is another's poison, I guess. I could take photos of myself doing fun stuff all day—and believe me, I have—but it doesn't change how I feel about me, which in general is a sort of state of comic self-loathing. This, I think, means that fundamentally, I hate myself but I see the humour in that. Because nothing is more funny than something that is utterly pointless.

I think it's natural to try to find reasons to like yourself. Why it should be that I'm drawn the other direction, I don't know. Perhaps it's because I find some truth in tripping up that's not evident in a successful tightrope balancing act.

Don't get me wrong, I admire people who can walk straight, or run and jump and do all these things. Yet I am utterly fascinated by the blood on my ragged knees.

Blokes aren't exactly known for talking about their feelings. We generally just keep going until we fall off. The poster advice is to talk to a mate, have a chat with someone, get out and do something, exercise, engage in something life-affirming. Reset.

If it didn't work, they wouldn't be making flyers about it, right? Figures would be impossible, but you could hazard a guess, most fellas would prefer to chat about anything than what's bothering them, and fewer still want to jump into the sea, for a giggle at least.

But the mind's a powerful thing, much more powerful than what Bill Hicks referred to as the great amusement park ride we're on. We get so convinced the ride is real that we don't want to get off. What better way to make it even more real than to let go of the safety bar, or hang out of the damn thing, right? Scream as you thunder around the loop.

Sounds legit, but it's the same bullshit, just louder.

I can't be the only one whose most real and life-affirming moments have been between myself and just one other set of eyes. A moment. A vibe. A silence followed by an indecent laugh. A moment without self-consciousness. An act of just being.

Hard not to wonder, however, if we're ever truly honest about who we are when we're with someone else? If you find that's the case, then that person is pretty special, because it's a pretty bloody unusual phenomenon.

But reality, whatever that means, and affirming your feeling about it, or your place in it, is one thing—and how ever we do that is, in the end, entirely our own business;

pressing reset is something different again.

The swimmer who started this conversation asked me where I go to reset.

There's a song called *Fade Into You* by the wonderful Mazzy Star. It's a song I've been listening to a lot lately. It aches and yearns. It begs to be held, to be let go and to fade away into blackness, into the heavy nothingness of mid-air in an empty room where the sweetest final musical note of something gradually diminishes until all that is left is the memory of it.

Me? That's how I reset. By fading away like disappearing ink, into the shadows, into a crowded place, or somewhere nobody knows me, so I can revel in the pointless insignificance of myself, until there is no more self, just a memory, and a questionable one at that.

Breakfast Epiphanies

There's probably very little that's healthy about a big, blow-out breakfast—one of those mid-morning, mostly weekend affairs with creaking platters of bacon, sausages, eggs and slabs of fresh French toast sprinkled with powdered sugar, pitchers of juice and steaming cafeterias of fresh-ground coffee.

It's not terribly good for the heart, in a coronary sense, but it's great for the soul.

It's also, for me, loaded with nostalgia. Before I could even work the dials on the electric cooker, I'd sneak downstairs after Dad left on the occasional Saturdays he worked, to make frothy hot chocolate from snaffled sachets and the still-hot water of the kettle.

While my mother slept, I'd luxuriate in the brief solitude of a silent house, stoking last night's embers in the sitting-room fireplace, expertly crawling close to blow until they glowed enough to make toast with a fork. The jam and melted butter running through my fingers never tasted sweeter. The only thing better was the gorgeous feeling of crisp bed sheets as the distant clang of pans and hot hisses signaled the imminent smell of cooked bacon permeating the house. Few breakfasts match the ones cooked in my childhood home by the person who loved me unconditionally and unequivocally: mom.

I grew up in an American household in an Ireland where crispy bacon swimming in equal measures of runny yolk and hot maple syrup from pancakes stacked on the same plate was loathed by friends who came to stay. *How could you?* they'd say, desperately defending sausages with a fork dam to stem the flood of sweet into savory.

I remember Dad being the proud recipient of a genuine waffle iron, pouring batter speckled with finely-chopped and cooked bacon into the grooves, then the maddening smell of the waffles crisping. Maple syrup was a rare treat brought by friends visiting from far away, but Dad managed to flavor simmering Golden Syrup with vanilla and orange.

It was the closest to anything like heaven I'll probably ever experience.

The implements behind these incredible breakfasts were treasured. Spatulas, spoons and whisks hung on the wall in a neat row, great brown bowls in which batters or omelettes were whipped up, were safely stacked away on high shelves along with the pitchers and coffee pots. Most special of all were the cast iron pans, some so large I could barely lift them with two hands, lovingly seasoned then wiped down after use and put away into the cooled oven. I would love to have some of those things still—but, like so many other things, somewhere in time, they vanished.

I still remember the last breakfast my mother cooked for me on the day she left and moved away: a simple fried egg, sunny side up on buttered wheat toast, and an ice-cold glass of bittersweet grapefruit.

She didn't tell me she wouldn't be back when we said goodbye, but as I walked to the bus for school, I could still feel the warmth of that small meal, so perfectly prepared, weighing heavy on my heart, the soft, cloying egg yolk still coating my thick throat as her tears dried on my cheek.

I became a bit of a breakfast aficionado in the years that followed, even when I had no home in which to lay a table. When I had little money to spare, at the expense of any other meal that day, I'd seek out the place that served the perfect eggs, bacon and sausages, the one that offered stacks of toast, with butter and different jams, then count out pockets of coppers to pay before relishing every forkful as I stared through the rivulets of condensation at people bustling past the window.

The first real summer job I had abroad, I blagged my way into the position of short order cook at a busy breakfast place in Newport, Rhode Island, owned by a former child star who'd acted alongside Audrey Hepburn and Vincent Price. Poor Richard's was a kitchen cacophony of clanking and hissing, a veritable Vaudeville act of juggled pans, eight omelettes on the go over just six gasping gas rings and a great griddle loaded with breakfast meats and every style of eggs, from over easy to scrambled with slivers of sweet red pepper and onion.

Through the smoky hatch, my window into hell, hungry diners clamored, one of whom, one day was senator Ted Kennedy.

I don't know what it was I served him, but it wasn't the huevos rancheros he ordered, a first for me. An hour later, the hatch filled with the suited shoulders of a Secret Service man.

—Who cooked the senator's order? he barked. I almost threw myself into a vat of pancake batter.

—Why? I croaked.

—The Senator wants you to know it was the best damned huevos rancheros he's ever had.

I looked up and could have sworn I saw silver-haired Ted wink as he went out the door.

It took me years to enjoy making breakfast again, and then it was just to see the eager faces of my own still-young family gleaming as I served bacon, eggs and French toast like Mom used to make, and I think they came to love the way the rich yolks would run into the sweet syrup and salty meat almost as much as I once did.

I don't know whether the breakfasts I've cooked for them are the healthiest, but one thing's for sure—it does the heart good.

Sushi

I'm lost in another world, disappeared into an artist's rendition of the Long Hall pub among a forest of other miniature paintings on a stall holder's wall, the pub lit up in what's either early morning or evening, orange and gold brush strokes like the flowing wood grain of an Edvard Munch, each tiny panel of window glass reflecting an inferno. It's the colour of nostalgia.

—Hi, barks a bearded face into mine, scaring me.

It takes a moment, a life in a nanosecond: those same eyes beneath the baseball hat brim of a young teen across the dinner table; leaning impatiently on one elbow from the top bunk for story time to begin; trudging along holding onto a stroller full of brothers; demanding juice from his perch on my shoulders on our way from Cali to Quito; those same eyes barely open behind the glass of an incubator, cruciform arms a mass of tiny tubes. Our son.

—Zachary, I say. It's an exclamation of pleasure. We

hug, his eyes already searching behind me as we disengage. I was just… I gesture to where the little painting of the pub was, but it's lost in a hundred others.

—Where is… he cuts in.

—There you are! says his mum and they hug too.

He looks splendid, all six feet of him, as people squeeze past irritably to George's Arcade. We move out to be under a blue sky, into deliciously cold air, three of us huffing into our hands and rubbing them together, partly to warm them, partly in anticipation.

—So, where do you want to eat, he says. There's…

—Can we see where you work? says his mum, eyes glittering hopefully.

—I suppose, he teases, scanning the space above her head for some reason why we shouldn't.

We head back into the dark together for the far entrance, a perfect symmetry to our trio, his mother quizzing him as I follow just behind, beaming. It's just like the old days, in a weird kind of way.

There was only ever three of us, a lifetime ago, before his brothers, then a sister, made six; those first few magic Christmases and long summers, back when it was all so new that our minds recorded every detail, now memories like fading, age-burnt Polaroids.

Zach points to a dilapidated warehouse building in the alley as we emerge.

—See the top three windows, he says. It doesn't look like much, but…

—Cool, I say, letting my mouth hang open while I squint.

—So handy, enthuses his mum.

Before we were ever a family, we were a three-person adventure. I had forgotten that.

We were no more than five years older than he is now, when we had him. I'd forgotten that too. So much gets left behind in the acceleration of time. His difficult birth at twenty six weeks, the nurse's furrowed brow and practised sympathy, the worried weeks, restless overnight hospital stays in institutional armchairs, our noses pressed against the glass until he was allowed home.

I remember promising his tiny face that he'd always be our miracle, whatever happened.

—There's a vegetarian place just up there, he says, pointing. Or there's the sushi place?

Twenty one years ago, we'd only just brought him home for the first time. I remember the almost unbearable pride of parading him up the street through the tiny town in which we lived.

He was still in diapers when we brought him all the way to Columbia, Equador and Nicaragua, big brown eyes unworried as his mother's dive mask disappeared beneath the waves. She thought she was drowning when water began leaking into her respirator, deep below the surface. The instructor had to stop her from panicking. I remember her hauling the tank off her back after, exhausted, and taking Zachary into her arms. "I'm never doing that again," she coughed.

He examined her wet hair and dabbed her face with a tiny hand. *Juice*, he said.

—Beer please, he tells the waitress, handing her the menu. My wife runs her hands across the table and smiles.

—This is really nice, she says. Just the three of us…

—Forget lunch, I joke. Let's head straight to the airport and get a plane somewhere.

—Back to Barcelona, my wife says. You'd like it there.

—California, I say, tapping a beat on the table. Or Mexico. You'd *love* Mexico.

—I do sort of need to be back at work, he smiles.

—Ah, there is that, I say.

—Well then, says my wife.

Sushi arrives and we eat ravenously. When we pay, Zach leaves the tip, then we head through the door, back into the great adventure, without looking back once.

How Hamburgers Came to Ireland

I've been obsessing about hamburgers lately. There are probably several reasons for this. Mainly, it's because I've been trying to eat less during the day, which makes me ravenous and, well, hamburgers... are God.

We're not talking about the grey disks of vaguely hamburger-like substance, served in a soggy bun on a plastic tray and dipped in florescent sauce from a tube before being joylessly and mechanically dispatched for the digestive tract to try and make sense of.

Nope. Nope. And nope. A real hamburger is an icon, the golden son of culinary evolution. It is, in its truest form, the model of balance and unity, all parts working towards one goal. For the duration of consumption, it is the entire world. And it shouldn't be messed with.

I actually credit my Mom and Dad for being the first to bring real hamburgers to Ireland. When we moved to Dublin from LA in the early 1970s, the nearest thing you could get here was something called a 'bun burger' and the meat tasted a little like sausage meat gone off.

In what was once the filthy, seething port of Dun Laoghaire, near where I grew up, there was something called a Wimpy Bar, a mysterious cave with streaked glass.

—Never go in there, Dad would cough as we'd roll past in our little blue Hillman, waving his hand in front of his nose and cranking up the window as though whatever might be emanating from there could possibly be worse than the black smoke belching from every lead-lined car around us, or the cigarettes Mom was stubbing out in the car's overflowing ashtray.

I wouldn't have dreamt of it. Saturday night was hamburger night in our house. Religiously. Dad even had a special grinder that attached to a table and was operated by a hand crank, so we could have our meat bloody without fear of dying a hideous and tortured death.

The other constituents were harder to source. Ketchup at that time was an incredibly sweet and viscous gel that required vigorous bottle-spanking to procure. So Dad made his own, from tomatoes, sugar, vinegar and spices. The process took twelve hours but yielded full bottles and jars of all shapes and size that could be stashed away in the cupboard for months.

American mustard was impossible to find. Once, a squeeze-bottle of the stuff arrived from the States and was treasured like liquid gold until it ran out, then the bottle was cut open to extract every last glob.

Iceberg lettuce was unheard of. There was only the limp, buttery stuff that dissolved into scum on contact with heat, so Dad had seeds sent from the US and grew a stunted, near-enough equivalent—all for hamburger night.

Hamburger buns, as such, did not exist. A 'bun' was a sweet, doughy thing with icing. Horrific. The nearest thing was a small, roughly circular loaf such as a *blaa*, but these weren't always easy to come by, so Dad occasionally baked them himself.

Even the tomatoes seemed small and mean, unlike the giant American 'beefsteak' variety that could be sliced into slabs. Try as he might, Dad couldn't grow them, and so we made do.

His home-made pickles, on the other hand, came close to the real deal, even though eaten from the jar they could make your face look like it was being sucked down a drain.

These simple ingredients, sandwiched inside a decent bun, were the hallmarks of the perfect burger; the search for the nearest thing in 1970s Ireland, just for our once-weekly family ritual, became a lifestyle. We grew stuff, ground stuff, pickled and bottled stuff, all for this.

Dad would season the ground meat with spices from a shop that also sold hops for making beer. Cumin, oregano, garlic powder, onion salt - these were speciality items back then. The trips to that shop actually inspired Dad to start brewing.

If we still had home-made tomato sauce, or the relish Mom began making too, he'd add that to the meat. No breadcrumbs, no egg. Are you crazy? That's so meatballs hold their integrity in a sauce. Hamburgers just need to hold it together long enough to get to your mouth. He'd leave the meat in a giant ball to rest at room temperature, as he prepared the toppings, or winced through a yeasty glass of dark foam from the reeking barrel under the stairs, Billie Holiday crackling in the background.

Those Saturday nights were sacrosanct. You'd be crazy to

make other plans. The sizzle and mist as the surface of the meat caramelized under red hot bars - we rarely barbecued, it was easier to control the heat in the kitchen grill.

Sometimes I'd have friends over. It was like bringing them to church. It tickles me to think how many had never had a hamburger. Some took the good word home. Soon I knew of at least two other families doing hamburger nights.

More than four decades on, it doesn't take much more than a good hamburger, usually made by me, and a nice beer brewed by someone who knows what they're doing, to excite my pleasure receptors.

I don't need nonsense toppings like restaurants heap on top of burgers which look more like giant, carbonized meatballs. The whole point is that it fits in your mouth and gets there without disintegrating. How difficult is that?

I'd even go so far as to say that my hamburger upbringing has taught me one of life's most important lessons: simplicity is everything—but 'simple' needn't mean second-best, just that the best doesn't need dressing up.

Anthony Bourdain and Me

I didn't know Anthony Bourdain, *Kitchen Confidential* author and culinary underbelly adventurist—even though I read all his books, watched most of his TV shows and even made a special trip in New York to eat at both of his restaurants, the now defunct Brasseries Les Halles.

I never knew him. I just thought I did.

It seems strange to me that we never met. When I was a features editor, I commissioned a writer more than once to seek the guy out on some book publicity tour and chat with him. I could have been the one to write the piece, but I didn't want hanging out with Bourdain to be a chore. I didn't want to be a fan boy either.

Anyone I sent to meet Tony came back raving about the man. I think it's because they expected Lou Reed, someone sullen or gruff in that New York rock star way. But Lou Reed, genius as he was, could be a bully and a jerk. Tony Bourdain was culturally curious, naturally funny and self-effacing, generous and well-mannered. I know this because I know cooks and, as usual, cooks got more out of him than writers. A friend of mine who ran some of Dublin's busier kitchens in the 1990s, was going out with a book publicist when Bourdain came to town, and ended up shuffling around the city with him, rolling the occasional spliff and visiting a few back doors of kitchens where the pirates that Bourdain wrote about haunted alleyways with knives and filthy aprons, shooting smoke from their nostrils and talking shit. His people.

My friend asked him what he thought about Jamie Oliver. Bourdain took a long drag and flicked the butt on the ground before stabbing it with his shoe. *Put it this way,* he said. *If I shared a cell with Jamie Oliver, I'd never be short of cigarettes.*

It was just 'trash talk', like battling rappers do, the sort of thing he'd probably have never said to a journalist. In fact, it's clear he had nothing but respect for anyone who put their time in working a kitchen, from the bottom rung, hauling asses into some claustrophobic backstreet furnace after four hours' sleep and filling a fifty-litre pot with stock, to the likes of TV's Nigella and Jamie.

I think I could have clicked with Bourdain because of that, because I'm hip to that respect, because before I ever chopped letters on a keyboard I chopped lettuce on a cutting board, and heaps of onions, or tailed prawns, or gutted lobsters, for so many hours I couldn't feel my fingers, in Dublin, Michigan and Rhode Island, with the kind of crazy people that would never get a job anywhere else, coke-addled lunatics living on scraps and fumes who made delicious things salted with the sweat dripping from their noses.

The only other place I've loved outside of a newsroom

of furious savants pounding out stories with their fists has been a restaurant kitchen. It's the only other place I know where a working day equates to a military operation, where the nerve shredding tension of doing something as close to perfect and on time as inhumanly possible is inclined to boil over into crockery-chucking violence.

In twenty years of working every department of a newspaper, I've seen plenty of meltdowns, no few tears and the occasional punch-up. In just my five years of sporadic forays into the nether world of food preparation, however, I've seen lopped fingers and third degree burns. I've ducked flying knives and seen tattooed fists pounding holes through walls, I even once saw a former US Army Ranger pass out and drop like a corpse in the chaos and cooks stepping over his body in the rush to continue service.

The only people I know who can drink better than newspaper hacks are cooks. I know people say 'chef', but to me, a chef is the boss who runs a kitchen. Cooks sweat and bleed and burn while the chef yells at them. If you've been a cook, or you're a decent chef, you have lifelong scars to show for it, and the ability to drink until 4am and get in at 8am to begin prepping all over again.

Long before I ever heard of Bourdain, before he invited us all down the back lanes between the dumpsters that reeked of rancid fat and rotten trimmings to peek between the dripping plastic ribbon curtains of a busy kitchen's back door at the sweat soaked convicts and mutineers beating our dinners into submission, these were people that to me defined hard work and brotherhood.

The only items of clothing I've carefully folded and kept, other than band tour T-shirts (good music, as Bourdain would attest to, is the heartbeat of any decent kitchen) are the hospital scrubs from each of my children's births, and my chef's whites, a still-stained jacket with two neat rows of black military-like buttons, too big for me in more ways than one.

The cooks with whom I've shared those agony of nights where tickets for orders came so fast and thick they waited in a bunch at the end of the row above the heat lamps on the service counter, whether I've seen them in person or not at all in the intervening decades, are still people I hold a deep affection for. Spider and Paco when I was only slinging dishes. Russ when I was slinging tickets, Stu when I was slinging breakfasts in the morning and lobsters in the afternoon.

Their honesty and integrity was something that touched me deeply and stayed with me, and its something I think Bourdain saw in every jobbing cook. It's something I sensed in Bourdain and it's why I think we could have connected, why I felt I could have known him, why I sort of did, but not at all.

Shirley, You Can't be Serious

Last-minute travel plans to visit family members who I haven't seen in almost thirty years on the other side of the world have me searching the entire house for my driver's license so I can rent a car while I'm there.

—Aren't you supposed to carry it in your wallet? says the eldest helpfully.

—It's bigger than my wallet, I huff, rifling through a shelf of CDs.

He opens his wallet and shows me his. It's one of the credit card size ones. My license is one of the big, fold-out things printed on pink blotting paper.

—Mine fits fine, he says, wiggling it.

By the time I give up the search, my wife has already downloaded and printed out forms for me to get a replacement. I open a biscuit tin with a view to eating my way through to some place where my licence might still be hidden. It doesn't help.

The long drive to my appointment at the National Driver License Service centre next morning has me recalling my very first license, which I got after learning to drive while working a summer job in the States.

I was camping on my mother's floor near the shores of Lake Michigan and borrowed her car for lessons, a hideous pastel yellow 1970 Chrysler with a white roof and a cream-coloured, padded vinyl interior, like a cabin on *The Love Boat*. It screamed 'grandma'.

Driving mom's car was like manoeuvring a canal barge. It seemed like the thing was thirty feet long. You could have fitted a double bed on the bonnet.

—It's called a hood, dear, said Shirley, my salaciously flirtatious driving instructor. Shirley was a fifty-something widow with a plume of hair styled from blue candy floss. She took great pains to buckle me in. Driving is like sex, she said, leaning across and checking my seatbelt. Take it real easy. Don't rush. Be gentle. You'll get there.

—Great, I said. How do we get started? I gripped the padded wheel and squinted to see the road somewhere in the distance, past the end of the car.

—You mean driving? Shirley looked at me and winked slowly. Just turn the key, hon'. Indicate where you want to go and don't pull out too fast.

I turned the key, indicated and spun gravel into the air without going anywhere.

—You might want to take the parking brake off first, dearie, said Shirley, checking her lipstick in the sun visor's mirror and smudging the corners of her mouth with a little finger.

Driving was the easy part, she explained. It was slowing down at the right time and stopping at all the right places that I had to get right.

—The only way to learn is by doing it, she smiled, putting one elbow on the edge of the car window and fluffing her hair.

We crawled around the back roads of Michigan twice a week the whole summer. If I waited too long at a stop sign, Shirley would say: *If we're gonna park, honey, best pull over,* or *Wait much longer on this corner, sweetheart, a gal's gonna get ideas.*

I still can't think of Shirley without smiling, or laughing aloud at her deeply inappropriate humour, and yet she was ever the lady.

When I got back to Ireland and showed Dad my shiny new American driver's license he just said, *great, so now you can drive in the States.* I think he was worried that I wanted to drive his car, but really I just wanted him to be proud of my achievement.

I bought a special wallet with a little plastic window in it to show off my Michigan license every time I went to pay for something. Strangely, no one ever passed comment. Even when it finally went out of date, I carried that thing around with me. I loved it, *Department of Motor Vehicles,* I had read it aloud, putting on my best Midwestern accent and I'd think of Shirley: *You might wanna stick on the air con, honey. It's gettin' hawwwt in here,* and the way she'd roll her eyes and fan her face.

Sailing straight past the place where Google maps says the NDLC is, I'm still wondering where on earth my Irish license could be. The irony is, I still have that American one from that summer way back in 1987, probably because it was always the right fit for a wallet.

—Who makes a driver's license that's too big for a wallet? I mutter under my breath as I spin the wheel to go back to the right turn.

The woman at Counter No.6 calls out a name that isn't mine. I'm the only one there. She looks at me, smiles and rolls her eyes. She calls out another person's name, then another, and then mine. I trundle over and sit.

—Well, at least you know your name, she says, smiling again. That's a good start. Now, what can I be doin' for yeh today?

I hand her my filled-in forms and tell her what an idiot I am. She tells me to look at the camera. It takes three photos. I look identical in each. Like a tired lunatic.

—Which one do you fancy? she says.

—I don't know, I say.

—I think the third one, she says. No one's going to be looking at it except the police, she smiles.

—Oh God, I tell her, slapping my forehead with my palm and we both laugh.

She tells me the good news is my license will be one of the fancy new ones that actually fit a wallet.

The bad news is, I probably won't get it for ten days, which means I won't be able to rent a car while I'm gone.

—Surely you can't be serious, I hear myself say.

—I am, she jokes: And don't call me Shirley.

The Witch Hunt

It's far too easy to chronicle my trip from Dublin to Los Angeles as a series of misadventures in which I am the hapless protagonist, less Bear Grylls than Mr Bean. It's also easy to forget the real reason for this journey, which is to reconnect with family living way out in the California oil fields, some of whom I haven't seen in more than thirty years, some I've never even met.

My biological mother is here visiting her identical twin. I spent years believing what I was told, that the two were my wayward sisters, nineteen years older than me, and only when one of them came to visit me as a child in the safe and insular suburb of south Dublin where I grew up, did I learn the truth.

The chronology is hazy now, but I was still relatively young when Julie arrived with her new husband, Jack. They moved into a flat nearby and began having me for sleep-overs. We bonded and it looked like we might become a family of three, but things didn't work out and Julie and Jack returned to America without me, eventually going their separate ways, and I never saw Jack again.

I have plenty of time to ruminate on my rather mixed up family history on the long bus journey through the mountains into the central plains of California and when the bus trundles into dusty Bakersfield, Julie is waiting.

—So, is one of the first things she says as we pull out of the parking lot into the hot November sun. I've been talking to Jack. He doesn't live too far away, just on the other side of town.

I try to remember the rancher in a paisley shirt who might have become my Dad had things gone differently so long ago, and a startling memory resurfaces.

—He saved me from almost choking to death.

—Oh my, laughs Julie. You really remember that? You were so young. You turned blue and I started screaming *Jack! Do something!* He picked you up by the ankles and shook you until the food popped out and you started breathing again.

—I remember, all right.

—He says he'd love to see you tomorrow. He'll pick you up. If you want…

My head reels for a second.

—Wow, I hear myself say. I mean yes. Definitely. I'd love that.

I'm carried for the rest of the evening along the eddies and flows of catch-up conversation, fogged by jet-lag. Lying in a strange bed that night, the rumble and whine of a fan somewhere down the hall, I remember the little plasticine dinosaur Jack made for me. I treasured that thing for years until it eventually crumbled to nothing.

When the doorbell rings, I wake up still in my clothes,

alone in the house. Pulling the blinds aside, I see a big pick-up truck outside and a guy with a baseball cap pulled down over his eyes lumbering up to the front door.

—Jack? I say, peering around the door.

—David?

Clambering into the front seat of his truck, he tosses a DVD into my lap.

—That's for you, he says. The title above a montage of jail mug shots says *Witch Hunt- produced and narrated by Sean Penn*. It'll tell you more about the shit that happened to me and a bunch of other people around here than we'll probably have time to talk about.

On the way to his house, Jack starts to explain how, back in the 1980s, almost two dozen parents in his town were arrested and had their children taken away amid allegations of child abuse, molestation, devil worship, cannibalism and murder.

Jack's face, leathered by years, hardens as he talks about the children coerced into giving false testimonies, debunked only after many spent years without parents, some of whom spent up to twenty years in prison.

In the middle of it all, says Jack, he and his wife Jackie began noticing police cars stalking them near their house and when it was clear they and their children were in danger of being the next victims of a system gone rogue, they fled, existing from camp site to camp site until police finally caught up with them at a motel one night, barged in and dragged their children away.

The couple spent years fighting the obscene charges and trying to get their kids back, until all the bogus cases were finally thrown out and authorities were forced to pay millions in damages, but by then terrible psychological damage had been done to many of the children involved and to the parents they were forced to grow up without.

Arriving at his house, Jack's wife seems happier to meet me than I'd thought she'd be and I'm soon buried beneath yapping dogs. There's no ice left to break.

—Let's go eat, says Jackie and a short time later, over food at a local sushi joint, I ask them: Are the bad guys still around? The ones that caused all this?

—Some of the prosecutors retired on big pensions, says Jackie. A lot of parents and children were never properly compensated. A few people in law enforcement at the time are still working. We pass them on the street.

—Wow, I croak.

—Yeah. Wow, I guess, says Jackie, her eyes hard for a moment.

—So, Jack sighs finally. How's life been for you?

I look down at my unfinished lunch then at Jack again.

—I really… can't complain, is all I manage, and so we all just eat in silence for a while, oddly easy in each other's company, even when the occasional siren flashes past.

Beans

—What was in those barbecue beans your mother used to make? asks my wife as we wrangle three dogs each with interconnecting leashes. This part is incidental. There are invariably six dogs on our daily walks in summer.

It's the fourth of July and we're having a barbecue later; it's the reason we're talking about my mom's beans and some of the other strange American side dishes that accompanied them for those big, back-yard family 'cook-outs' as she used to call them state-side.

—Oh, man, I can't help chuckling at the memory, what *wasn't* in them.

Mom would take a few humble tins of baked beans, add minced onion, peppers and garlic, molasses and brown sugar, then simmer low and slow until the sauce was thick, almost black, and so sweet it made your teeth hurt, if you could get it off the spoon.

She'd sit at the little kitchen table in her house on Lake

Michigan and make a list on a yellow lined pad of paper: *Meat, buns, BBQ beans, potato salad…* She'd still have her night dress on and be sipping coffee. There might be a coupon snipped from the local newspaper, for hot dogs— but it would mean a trip to Family Dollar: green bean salad, sodas, slaw…

—Those huge potato salads, remembers my wife. Delicious, but so thick and chunky you could've used it to fill holes in walls.

—And that thing she used to do with Cool Whip and orange Jello, I shudder. Mmm. Frozen imitation whipped cream from a tub, folded into fake fruit Jello to make… I'm not even sure what, or why it was there with the salads and side dishes. *Have some*, Mom would say. So you did.

We'd started going back to the States every other year, me, my wife and our four kids. We'd spend weeks in American summer sunshine, often taking in the fourth of July and helping with preparations, wiping down yard furniture, dragging lawn darts out of the basement.

Lawn darts, or javelin darts, or simply 'Jarts', were a family barbecue must-have and an American rite of passage—or they were until their sale was banned throughout the States following a large number of horrific injuries and fatalities.

Basically a weighted twelve-inch spike with aerodynamic fins, the idea was to throw them up in the air so they'd come down on or near a target. How could anything go wrong? It was almost as much fun as playing with fireworks.

Grandpa Don made sure the kids knew the rules : and the first rule was, don't touch the lawn darts. Don was Mom's second husband, a World War Two veteran and a sweetheart to his grandchildren. The only other rules I remember were don't leave the hose pipe running—and never, ever let the American flag touch the ground.

I thought you liked my barbecue beans, I can hear Mom say, appearing behind me on the still sprinkler-wet lawn at the shady side of the clapboard house, scaring me a little, the electric whine of cicadas in the tall pear trees nearby, the chirp of tree frogs. *I do, I do*, I'd say, irritated, swatting a fly away from my face and shaking the spoon until a thick brown glob came loose onto my paper plate next to the cold salad of sliced green beans from preserve jars in the basement—the 'slaw of shredded cabbage and apple. It's the first time I remember, since being a kid myself, not wanting food items on my plate to touch.

I can still smell the heat of the sun.

Back at the car we load up the dogs.

—Is there anything we still need? asks my wife. I dig a yellow sheet of notepaper from my pocket. *Mince, buns, BBQ beans (a question mark in brackets), potato salad...*

—Cool Whip? I joke.

I can't quite bring myself to do the beans in the end. I love their dark, sweet smell, but the thought of that cloying, almost caramel-like consistency is too much to bear thinking about.

Instead, I spend all afternoon on the potato salad, letting the nostalgia of every ingredient envelope me like a warm, sad glove: the cubes of potato cooling on a tray, the fine dice of red onion, celery and cornichons; chewy lardons of cooked bacon; mayonnaise with a dash of red wine vinegar and Dijon; the crackle of the wooden pepper grinder over the top.

I season the minced beef and pork then pre-make the patties, while a pot of pornographic Cabonossi sausages simmers on the stove.

I fill the freezer with bottles of beer and set the oven

timer to remind me to take them out.

The few friends and their families who we invite to what we end up calling the Mom and Don Memorial Barbecue, arrive in small waves, negotiating their way through a tide of barking animals.

Our own children, mostly grown, have friends around too. Meats sizzle and smoke. Buns are presented hand over hand for toasting. Chilly bottles clink. There's no cicadas or tree frogs and we're not much for flags, but the sun feels bright and hot.

Planted in a flower pot at the front gate is a garish lawn ornament, a nylon parrot holding a margarita. *It's 5 o'clock somewhere* it says. Mom insisted I have it. When the wind blows, the parrot's windmill tail spins around.

I think of Mom and Don, watching it spin and spin; I take a slug of beer and in that moment I'm truly sorry, for not making the barbecue beans.

Boy Meets Girl

Horror movies are perfect date movies, made for couples. The more terrifying the story, the better. Good horror films force us into each other's arms, scare after scare making us jump and cling together like frightened clams as something leaps out of the dark, blood splatters across the screen and the body count mounts.

Stephen King's *It* couldn't have been better timed for the first date night my wife and I have been on for a while; it was almost thirty years ago to the day since Stephen King had first thrown us into each others arms.

When people ask how my wife and I first got together, I often joke that I stalked her, that I knew the bus she took, and one day, I stayed on it all the way to the terminus and back twice, until she got on, just so I could talk to her.

In reality, though I'd noticed her on the same bus a few times, it was hit and miss. The first day we really got talking, the day of that first spark, was in late September of 1987. On that day, as I vividly recall, my face was buried in a certain Stephen King book about a killer clown named Pennywise.

At the time, it was considered his masterpiece. In 1986 it was the bestselling book in the U.S. and the following year was the winner of the British Fantasy Award. The paperback version, even with its bible-thin pages, was brick-thick.

The story grabbed me by the face and dragged me in deep, right from page one. I could barely put the book down, but when I had to, all I could think about was picking it up, and when I did, I'd become utterly lost in it all over again, frequently missing my stop on the bus home.

On this particular night, I'd missed my stop and been back to the terminus twice because of the book. It was late and dark by the time I finally unpeeled my face from the pages and noticed the only other person with me near the back of the bus was a young woman who I had barely spoken to since we were about 12 years old.

—What are you reading? she asked.

I told her the book was Stephen King's latest, but she shouldn't be put off by the title, that this was so much more than a horror story. And with that, I was off, babbling about a group of kids in the fictional town of Derry, Maine, and how the narrative connected and intertwined with their adult lives three decades later.

This time, when the bus came to my stop and sailed past, it was intentional on my part. By now we'd moved on to talking about her long summer working on the east coast of the States, about her college life, and her family. We had connected. The next time we met, at a party, our feet connected under a table. The time after that, I think, our lips connected. Within five years, we were husband and wife.

What is it about the human condition that makes us look for patterns? And yet, oddly, there's a peculiar circularity to finding myself trying to convince my wife of the merits of going to the movies together to see *It*, precisely thirty years to the week, if not to the day, of that first fateful bus conversation.

But there's more. The central story of *It* pivots around a group of seven twelve-year-old school friends, six boys and a girl. In the book, they meet again as adults thirty years later (a storyline followed up in the 2019 movie).

In real life, the things we said as children, we barely remember—but often we'll easily recall the faces, voices and characters of the classmates who populated our world before we plunged headlong into young adulthood and our lives began to rush by.

My wife and I were in the same primary school sixth class together. Before we all moved on to new schools or different classes in the same new school, I was crazy about her for a time, in that hot, flushed, fumbled notes at the back of the classroom, misspelt Valentine kind of way.

As things would turn out, I'd be almost twenty one before I'd be able to say more than two words to her, but I remember hanging around the playground on the last day of school with a small group of boys, dying to go but unable to leave before someone suggested one of those silly childhood pledges: *we should promise to all meet up again…*

We probably said we'd do it in ten years, or that we'd meet on the top of a building somewhere, like the Empire State, on New Year's Eve maybe—when in reality, we would never all see each other at the same time again.

That is, until just a few weeks ago, when six of us from our sixth class of 1979, one girl, and five boys, all former friends, sat down to dinner and raised a glass to another classmate—a seventh, a friend who had, to our horror, died suddenly earlier this year.

But it's not the horror that makes a story good, even if it can make us jump into one another's arms, right? It's the timeless themes woven between the scares that make a good story great: boy meets girl is one of them.

Who Let the Dads Out?

Quite how my father ended up in charge of the Christmas dinner, I'll never know. He nodded off for the last time, not long after Christmas, five years ago. Perhaps he wouldn't have been able to tell me anyway. It's just how it was and it wouldn't quite be Christmas without the sight of Dad elbow deep, like James Herriot, up a turkey.

For the rest of the year, Mom cooked everything, except for what I came to think of as dad food—meatballs, chili, burgers, home-made pizzas, his infamous and almost inedible curries which would have him whooping and fanning his face with his big hairy hands as the tears rolled off his nose.

—Whoo! Boy, that's a hot one! he'd howl and sneeze as we blinked at our plates.

—Don't worry, Mom would whisper. I'll fix us some sandwiches later.

When they were first married, Mom told me, she

couldn't cook at all. She didn't even know how to make a cup of coffee. On their first day together, she made Dad a cup of hot chocolate instead.

Day by day, she taught herself, meal by meal. By the time I ambled along, her cooking was famous. Family friends would go to her for recipes and tips.

At Christmas, Mom would take over the kitchen about six weeks beforehand and begin making scrumptious gift baskets for her friends. People I know still talk about them—the frosted sugar cookies in Christmas shapes, gingerbread men, chocolate dipped peppermint creams and blocks of pink and white coconut ice.

The smell in the house was maddening.

I was only allowed to sample the broken and misshapen rejects, a shattered gingerbread limb, a malformed peppermint cream. How I envied those baskets of perfection, all wrapped up in crinkly cellophane. I could barely imagine the abject luxury of snapping off a bite of perfectly decorated star-shaped cookie, or letting a fully formed chocolate peppermint cream melt away in my mouth.

I'd like to think that the reason I always remember Dad being in charge of the Christmas turkey was that he was giving her a day off. I suspect that it was really because everything Dad did was a performance. He couldn't just give you a haircut, for instance—you had to be on a chair in the middle of the garden while he staggered around like a mad sculptor, poking your head this way and that.

The poor turkey. Some of the positions Dad wrestled that thing into were, well, unseemly. One year he rustled up some sort of device to fill with beer and sit the turkey on as it cooked. It looked for all the world like it was on the bog, having a think.

Of course, it fell over in the oven and at some point emerged later, flat on its back, with the loathsome-looking thingamajig still sticking out of its arse. To this day, I don't even want to think about what it looked like.

Away from the hubbub, somewhere in the background, perfect potatoes were produced, steaming butter volcanoes of mash, perfectly crunchy, crumbly roasties, sprouts, carrots done in orange juice and butter, fudge-like fingers of parsnip in maple syrup, as if by magic, all made by Mom.

Yet still, Christmas dinner seemed to be Dad's production as he gathered up the skins of the grapefruit halves from breakfast, crushed them in the ball of his fist, then plunged them into the turkey's furthest recesses.

—Oh boy, he'd say. Wait'll you taste this. It's gonna be so moist, so flavourful.

I can't say I noticed much difference, but we'd all nod and say *mmm* on cue when it came time to sit and eat.

I wish I could say I inherited my culinary skills from my mother. I fear this simply isn't the case. Mom would quietly spirit up delicious smells, magicking complex flavours from the simplest fare. She never took a bow. When Dad cooked, all he was missing was the swish of a curtain and a sliver topped cane. Loathe as I am to admit it, that's me. It's either a full-on production, or it isn't dinner.

It is Dad's experimental performance approach that informed my Christmas cooking—and not always for the better. I couldn't just baste the bird and set the timer, the thing had to wallow in a mop bucket of saline water and *bouquets garnis* for days, scaring the bejesus out of anyone who wandered in to the utility room.

Or there was the year I produced a giant oven bag from somewhere and constructed a sort of balloon around the turkey which, when pricked with a knife at the table seven hours later, promptly deflated to reveal a dark, thick soup with a few turkey bones floating around in it. If Christmas Day cooking was any sort of magic show, that was the year I was Tommy Cooper. I might have even staggered back to the oven to check if the bird had escaped.

In recent years, I've relinquished my place in the Christmas dinner spotlight. Now we take off at noon on the big day for my wife's family home, where everyone helps get Christmas dinner ready and where I'm happy to have little more than a supporting role.

Somehow, tables are wrestled together and chairs found to seat twenty of us. It's a cacophony of Christmas crackers and clattering plates as platters of turkey and ham are passed around and somehow we're all fed until we're fit to burst. *Just like that.*

It's nothing less than magic.

Wedding Rings

We didn't get nearly as much grief as we probably deserved when we informed our respective families of our intention to marry each other more than five thousand miles away, and at such short notice that no one had the faintest hope of getting over in time to see it happen.

You are invited... was how we broke the news on rather generic cards that we designed ourselves at the local Kinkos, a California photocopy shop founded by a surf bum, where I worked at the time. We mailed them so they'd arrive too late.

It wasn't that we were embarrassed about expecting a baby, that we were only in our young twenties at the time, or that we lost the baby before the invitations were halfway to their destinations. I think it was just that we didn't want the hullabaloo of a great big do.

The wedding rings were the most expensive thing we had ever bought together, and we only managed to do that on what was called lay-away, or weekly direct deposits to the sleazy shopping mall jeweler until the rings were paid off, long after the ceremony.

It wasn't quite how either of us pictured it, though neither of us ever imagined a big wedding with relatives in feather boas and pushy photographers lining up clichéd shots before the catered carvery dinner, speeches and disco.

Ours was finding something to wear that wasn't shorts for a simple ceremony with a judge in the nearby civic center, witnessed only by our four housemates, then tearing home in our beaten-up, banana pudding coloured 1972 Plymouth Volare, for a barbecue beside the lake where we lived.

Her mum managed to overnight a package to us with a wedding dress she had worn herself in another era, but we'd bought one already so it was just worn for a few of the snaps taken by two of our housemates who shared a photography darkroom.

The ceremony was over quickly. We took turns signing the wedding certificate which looked like a fake from a toy store with its eagle and old west font, like something you'd fill in to tell a kid they were a real-life sheriff, honestly, to go with their little tin star. I could barely read the name of the deputy justice on the certificate. He gave it to us mostly blank, to fill out later.

Back at our house on the lake, we changed out of our wedding clothes. Someone had bought a cake but couldn't find a traditional wedding topper, so they got a schmaltzy ceramic hugging couple from a Hallmark store and plonked it on top.

It might have seemed an inauspicious beginning, and in many ways it was—the mall-store rings, the five-minute ceremony, the fake looking certificate and the backyard barbecue followed by a cake with a chubby little made-in-China hugging couple on top.

But I remember the sunset over the abandoned Cold War airport base out back that night reaching out with golden tendrils that bounced and shimmered across the lake, and the ducks that fluttered up the back lawn to just below where we sat.

It was a far cry from anything we'd dreamed of in our lives before, back in Dublin; that city was inconceivably far away.

The next day we took a plane to Mexico City, a beautiful, crowded, stinking megalopolis, teeming with people and taxis, jugglers at traffic lights, and prostitutes beneath the scaffolding of high rises outside the smoke-filled witchcraft market of Sonora.

That day, when we discovered Mexico City for the first time, sat eating sandwiches in the famous Zócalo main square as a noisy socialist workers' demonstration clattered past and the nearby Federales fidgeted with their guns, was exactly twenty five years ago.

We planned where to go from there—almost three hundred miles past distantly visible Popocatépetl, a still-active volcano, to Oaxaca. After that, who knew what life would hold?

The last entry in that photo album was June 23; slipped between the pages I found a printout from a hospital ultrasound showing the dark, curled-up shadow of a baby. It was dated just June 15 the following year.

Over the course of twenty five years, the timeline shifts in cloud. It's a treacherous path, twenty five years. It crumbles and falls away in places. Other times, it's fit for an entire convoy.

Twenty five years on, in Skerries, we decided to have the wedding reception we never had, or at least something approaching how we might have done it had we been old enough to know how to do anything at all at the time.

We had food and fire and music, friends sprawled on our lawn as tealights hung in hedges began to twinkle in the fading light.

—When we were married twenty five years ago, announced my wife, —we had just four guests and they were all our housemates.

—Sadly none of them could make it today... but we have four new housemates to celebrate with, and they're all here.

It took me a second to figure it out, then I looked around the crowd and saw, smiling more than anyone else, the family we made.

Be Afraid, be Very Afraid

Years before fake cobwebs and pumpkins were even heard of, decades before polystyrene tombstones or fancy motion-detecting shrieking door-knockers were annual prerequisites, my older brother and I owned Halloween.

As a child, I could smell Halloween's approach. It was the acrid, woody smell of leaf mulch, and the smoke of the first fires of fall. It was the faint whiff or wish of charred marshmallow or something sweet and baked. It was rotting apples, gunpowder and rain.

It was more important than birthdays, almost as important as Christmas, and my brother and I prepared for it with the zeal of worshippers making ready for a religious rite, solemnly stuffing wooden bones into the legs and sleeves of a floppy, newspaper-filled corpse to hang in front of the house. It was, to me, something terrifying to see, and I loved it.

My brother would tell me how he'd heard whispers

behind the rasp of the torn pages he crumpled into the thing's arms, or that he'd seen it twitch. I was probably nine and still afraid of an open wardrobe door at night, so I'd poke at the hanging legs from behind the pillar of our porch, too afraid to peek under its dreadful rain-stained pillowcase hood.

I remember one night, days before Halloween, hearing the sound of boots thumping slowly up the stairs and dragging their way down the landing and stopping outside my room—then a barely audible scrabbling at the door handle, then silence. I finally dared to look, but there was nothing but the dim yellow light and faint music from my brother's room. I shuffled quickly there, past every black doorway, only to find my brother propped up on his bed, pretending to read a book.

—Hey, he said, not looking up. Any idea who took our Halloween dummy? Because it's gone now. All there was is this note. He showed me the terrible handwriting, like a crayon clutched in a fist, scrawled in red: *I'm coming to get you.*

Of course, I knew what was up—mostly. I knew that his best friend from next door had already tucked the thing up in my bed in the few minutes I was gone—most likely. I knew that dummies didn't spontaneously detach, thump away and scrabble at doors, or scrawl death threats… probably. But that didn't make it any less horrifying to return to my room and find it there.

As it happened, they'd done one better, standing the thing up in my wardrobe with the door open. When I saw it, I don't even remember taking the stairs five at a time, just that I was suddenly down in the TV room, howling in front of my parents.

You'd think I'd hate Halloween, but I really did love it.

I loved every twisted coat-hanger spider he made. I loved every drop of red poster-paint blood spatter. I loved the pleading, burnt-cork hand prints on the front door and the way my brother would peek around from inside it with the leg of one my mother's nylons over his face to tell the kids that everyone in the house was dead.

Halloween was the nearest we got to being brothers. The conspiracy of it. *Hey*, he'd say. *You know what would be cool?* And it would be something sick, like cracking open a window behind the dummy and moaning when kids came: *Please. Pleeaase. Kill me. Killlll meeee!* They'd never experienced anything like it and someone would always burst into tears.

Not being the victim of it all for a change felt very good indeed, and I have never laughed so hard—almost to the point of losing control of my bladder—at someone else's fear and misery quite like I did when my brother scared the living bejaysus out of those kids.

One year I didn't have a friend to go around the houses with me on Halloween night, so our parents made my brother go.

—Gimme a mask, he said, because it's so freaking embarrassing being seen with you.

I had a werewolf mask from the previous year; there were only ever four kinds, witch, werewolf, Dracula and Frankenstein, and I gave him that. He sprayed it black and pulled his hood up. As he waited at every gate, kids would stop and stare up at him.

—What are you? they'd say.

—I'm your worst nightmare, stupid punks," he'd say.

There are several kinds of fear: fear of the unknown, the fear of something unseen or beyond our experience, the fear of fear itself. If I were honest, I might say that my formative experiences around Halloween, and the many other times throughout the year as a child when my brother would conspire to terrify me out of my tiny wits, have saddled me with a bit of a lifelong addiction to fear, or at least, to the drained, adrenaline rush of relief when fear is finally finished with you.

I have occasionally made life very difficult for myself, by diving feet first into some dark, black, shark-infested hell hole; uprooting to some place I've never been or blagging my way into a job I'm hopelessly under-qualified for. It can be Halloween all year round, when you are your own hanging dummy.

But mostly, I've been able to see behind the masks of my tormentors, see life for the elaborate and unnecessary ritual that it is.

As for my older brother, it's been so long since I've heard anything about him that if the phone rang this Halloween and it was him, I'd probably scream.

Don't Ever Grow Up

It's a miracle, seeing your children grow up, or rather, realising with a heart-sick pang every now and then how much they've done so. Part of you feels proud. Part of you feels gutted. Part of you wants to say, *hey, slow down. Growing up is overrated.* But growing up isn't a choice. It's survival. All you can hope is they squirrel away a small part of the real them somewhere safe, like some small, beautiful, hopeful thing a prisoner might hide beneath a stone.

You hope the cynicism and hollowness of adult existence will be something that avoids them, that they'll stay mischievous, creative and hopeful. That they'll always find time to focus on the things they love, the things that struck them with amazement when they were young.

But adulthood is an unavoidable illness, a stalker poking through your children's possessions, whispering words of ridicule in their ear as they sleep: *hey, stupid; that's kids' stuff; grow up.* It's insidious.

And yet, we open the door to the dark of our sleeping children, a doomed ritual, deceptively finite, to whisper, hearts quietly bursting, *don't you ever, ever grow up*.

I love the childish things that still surround our only daughter: her bedroom, like an explosion in a charity shop; the recently discarded ukulele in a plate of fluorescent crumbs; the unkempt bed and dog-eared posters on the walls; the mess of make-up brushes and discarded candy wrappers.

It's such a contrast to the monastic cells her adult brothers' bedrooms have become, stripped down to a small pile of books, or a jar of change. They're barely home. A third brother is almost catching up and can't wait to join the other two; sights set on college and the world beyond. You sense it in his world-weary sighs and the way, when his sister has a meltdown, he says: *Oh, grow up*.

I could explain what a curse that is. How growing up means having to search yourself for the things that you can do, then pawn these off and have your passions held hostage for a pay cheque. Instead, I watch as days flood by and the sweet songs grow quieter, then all but disappear.

I'm not sure when our daughter stopped singing to herself, when clouds started casting a shadow over her sunny young face.

I'm not sure when her careless gambolling became a trudge (though a breeze block's worth of books in the bag on her back certainly helped take the skip out of her step).

I'm not sure when the girls she thought she knew began to whisper, snigger or conspire, just that there were suddenly tears and loneliness where there used to be nothing but bright eyes and smiles.

I'm not sure when she went from being irrepressible, a

centre of shining light in every situation, to being quiet, dark and moody, locking herself away in her room for hours, losing the desire to eat very much at all.

I remember hugging her awkwardly one day, as only awkward dads can hug their teenage girls, and telling her uselessly, *it's all a part of growing up*. But in that moment, I hated *growing up* for what it does to little girls, lulling them away with promises of freedom and sophistication. Lies, damn lies.

I hate the shallow things that other children learn to emulate, a fragile world of shifting loyalties.

I hate the people we expect our children to become— like us, hardened and distrusting. I hate that door we push our children toward so hard that they're not actually running any more, but falling forward, and if they do fall, it's *for crying out loud, get up*.

So I've made a quiet promise, for my part, to pick up where evidently I've been remiss. To subtly encourage all the little things that make our daughter happy, and to roundly dismiss the things that darken her life, as I would a tiny, irritating fly. To make the things she loves to eat, do the things she loves to do, and beg, if needs be, to hear the songs she loves to sing—all these things, while I still can.

I know we already have a girl who will someday have the ability to beam in the face of a spluttering boss; someone that no cheap romance will ever be able to capture and subjugate; someone who will be the envy of every girl who meets her because they will seek to emulate her, and they will fail.

I just have to make sure she knows all this too, before the grown-up world and all its useless pantomimes sneaks in and seductively does her out of her dreams.

When that happens, I'll be there.

Kicking Things Under the Couch

I can't remember what I've come in for, as I stalk the long, overstuffed and garishly lit aisle of my local convenience store, but when I see a display of Christmas chocolate selection boxes in the middle of the aisle, I stop dead.

The colourful pictures of vintage Santas on the boxes, crooked arms and legs frozen in a sort of teddy-bear march, winking like an embarrassing uncle on a wedding dancefloor, suddenly turn my stomach. I've no idea why, but I can barely look at it.

It's way too early to be reminded of Christmas—the shop hasn't put so much as a Halloween mask up yet—but it's not that. Something else makes me turn heel and take that infuriatingly jolly image, scrunch it up and pound it with my fist deep into a corner of my mind's basement among the rows of padlocked doors there.

I'm sure I'm not the only guy who does this, who has a place in his head to bury stuff that bothers him. It's the psychological equivalent of clearing up by kicking things

149

under the couch. Out of sight but not entirely out of mind.

A mulching machine would probably have been a better idea. Or a computer desktop where I could drag the things I don't want to deal with to the trash. But I guess I'm old-school, so a padlocked door way down in the dark will have to do.

I shrug to the shopkeeper on the way out, wagging my finger at the side of my head, universal sign language for *don't mind me, I'm just not with it*, and then my day goes on rather like the day before, and the day before that— days in which, thankfully, winking Santas do not factor.

It's the middle of the night when I shudder awake from a pointless sleep, from some dream I can't quite remember, throat hitching like I'm trying to force tears. I lie there in the dark, unable to gather my clouded thoughts, tired and confused.

The digital clock marks the ages between minutes before I succumb to the strange, sickening toothache of sadness that's haunting me and I slowly drift off again.

The next time I wake up, it's with a feeling of panic. It's still dark and less than an hour has crawled by on that hateful clock. All I can think is, I should telephone my mother. What's the time in the States? I fuzzily calculate the time difference. Five hours, or is it six?

It takes a bewilderingly long while for me to remember that my mother is dead.

I scrunch up my eyes, trying to remember, searching, rattling doors. When did she die? Last year. No, THIS year. Why can't I remember? What the hell is wrong with me? Why this? Why now? I turn over and over in the bed, muttering in the frustration of half sleep.

In my head there's an image from the first dream I

can't shake off: my mother is lying in a coffin, her body surrounded by a string of little white Christmas lights.

My mother loved the seasons and marked them as promptly as a Hallmark card stand. She had a little fake fir tree that hung on the wall in her sitting room: right now it would be decorated with autumn leaves, in a week or so little plastic Halloween pumpkins, then festive red ribbons.

I realise, lying there in the dark, that I haven't allowed myself to think of my mother very much since the day I took the call from where she was dying. I was surrounded by impatient strangers at that crucial moment: I had to put my hand to the earpiece to hear her say goodbye.

My mind simply couldn't process what was happening as it happened: it was all so out of context. When the phone went dead I spent a long moment clearing my throat and swallowing hard, before having to return to business.

Grief was kicked under the couch, soon to be hastily boxed and labelled for the basement: 'Do Not Return'.

There was no big funeral to go to, no chance to meet one last time in my mother's memory and share our stories.

One minute she was there, the next minute she wasn't. The whole, lovely, soft-hearted, Lilly-of-the-Valley-scented presence of her, however physically far away, just ceased.

The cruel ages between minutes turned to hours, days and weeks, and then months went by.

In all this time, I've managed to keep myself so distracted that I've sort of tricked myself into forgetting all the stuff that I kicked down the steps into the dark—until an unseasonable Santa, winking from the top of a garish display, managed to rattle those chains.

I'd like to say as I lay there in the middle of the night, that somewhere in my stupid head a door creaked open and I was finally able to let something I'd been dreading flood over me.

But men can be strange about things like grief, loss, and pain. The first Christmas without my mother is going to be difficult, I know this now. But it's way too early to be thinking about any of that yet—it's not even Halloween.

King of the Fairies

They say you can tell a lot about a person by the company they keep. I don't know about that. The friends that I love, impervious to time apart, are drinkers, dreamers, heretics and hedonists; they are fearless, curious and romantic—but most of all, they are alchemists, able to beat the clay of life into something strange and wonderful.

These are qualities I envy and which come close to describing one of the most extraordinary men I have met, while on holiday some years ago in The Burren. A genuinely magical being with a tongue of tarnished silver, had I been told Peter harked from some otherworldly realm, I probably wouldn't have blinked.

We could have dived down the rabbit holes of any hostelry that night, but I chose a place that could as easily been a hobbit pub from *The Lord of the Rings*. As soon as we unlatched the heavy door and pushed it open into the soft, dark warmth of the place, as though waiting for our cue, a man at a table to our right tossed a spoon noisily into a huge bowl and pushed it away from him.

—Isn't that the best soup a man has ever had?

Platinum-haired Peter was built like a Viking. He had the glint in his eyes of someone with a secret, that you might be the one he'd tell it to.

He marched behind the bar, pulled a pint and planted it in front of me. I hadn't asked for anything yet, he told me it was on the house.

He told us he was the direct descendant of a famous highway robber, and asked me to follow him.

He led me through passages to a room that reeked deliciously of hops. I watched, fascinated, as he clambered around towering vats to check various dials and hatches like a mad professor. He opened one and beckoned me over, a finger to his lips. He showed me the pond of fizzing spittle inside.

—It's alive, he whispered, gazing at it lovingly.

I was gutted I had to leave. On the drive home to Dublin the following day, I jabbered on and on about Peter.

—He talks to his yeast, I told my wife.

—I know," she said. You told me.

It was over a year before I returned.

—You took your time, said Peter, topping off a pint and setting it in front of me and giving me the uncanny feeling once more that he'd somehow known I was about to walk in. This time I had my younger brother from America in tow, a Death Metal head complete with goatee and blood-spatter T-shirt.

—We're on a camping trip, I explained.

—Not any more, you aren't, said Peter. You're staying here.

He ferried pints to us all night, samples he called

them, until blurry-eyed, we begged for our beds. We were brought upstairs to store rooms, where something resembling mattresses remained among the detritus of creative decades.

—This one, he bellowed to my brother, is the bed where my great aunt died from TB.

—Um, managed my brother. Thank you.

—And this one, he whispered at the next door, is the very bed in which I arrived from between my mother's legs, screaming into the world.

—Oh, I said, looking at it.

—Sleep tight, he added and vanished.

The next day we were rallied at dawn. I'm not sure if Peter had slept at all. We crawled down to the closed pub where he stomped across the floorboards.

—The morning is a-wasting, lads!

Next thing we knew, we were hurtling over The Burren, stopping twice so that my brother could lean over a fence and talk to God. The third time, the vehicle was abandoned.

This way! Peter took off over the rocks.

—But… but the path? I pointed weakly in the other direction.

—Fuck the path! Peter marched ahead. *Follow the smell of goat shit!*

I looked at my brother, whose stomach hitched and he clutched his face, doubling over as Peter disappeared into the distance, bellowing some song or poem.

Hours later, we limped, empty, back to the car, and launched back to where breakfast was a great shank of lamb accompanied by two full pints apiece. My brother looked at his, stroked his Death Metal beard and began to cry softly.

—Now I feel we've gotten to know each other. Peter wiped his mouth with one great sleeve. I've something to show you. He whisked out a newly printed poster that depicted the sepia images of Native Americans in their feathered heyday: dead centre was Peter, head shaved, in the garb of a tribal chieftain, clutching a spear.

Somewhere about a hundred miles or so into our journey home, my brother summoned the strength to ask if it had all really happened. I knew what he meant. It felt like we'd just been up the beanstalk.

Years evaporated: I yearned to return, but never quite managed it. Then a photo pinged into my phone. It took me a moment to recognize the view from above a fermenting vat, fizzing foam inside.

Come right away, read the message. *I've harvested wild yeast from the mythical fort of the Tuath Dé Danann. I've made FAIRY BEER!*

Cucumber Boy

Sometimes I wish I could go home, to the house where I grew up, one more time.

I wish Mom would answer the door, ask why I didn't use my key, then go back to the third stair, pick up the telephone receiver threaded over the banisters by its curly chord, and continue talking to her friend Vera between puffs of smoke.

The ashtray she'd be using says *The Derby And All That Jazz*, after the American bar it was taken from, probably on one of her trips back to the States. *Not there*, she'd say, waving me away. She means my coat. It doesn't go on the banister, it goes on the coat rack, dummy. *And pick up that schoolbag please, before someone trips and breaks a leg.*

The doors to the kitchen are like saloon doors: they made a dull flapping noise when I went through them—I always turned around and went through them again, just for fun.

The kitchen walls I remember are light brown, the only room in the house not painted white. It used to have hideous orange psychedelic patterned wallpaper, but one night mom got up from her chair in the TV room, marched into the kitchen and started tearing it down. We thought she'd gone crazy. Maybe she had.

There was hatch from the kitchen to the TV room that Mom and Dad called the booze cupboard, which is what they used it for. Underneath was the junk drawer. *Do we have any batteries?* someone might yell. *Check the junk drawer*, Mom would yell back (we yelled a lot). You'd have to scoop up handfuls of playing cards, rubber bands and spools of thread to look properly.

The fridge was in its own wardrobe-sized room we called the pantry, past a curtain of multi-coloured plastic ribbons that I would let all over me like a cloak, and Mom would tell me I'd be *in trouble, mister* if I pulled them down.

Out back was a concrete porch and three steps to the lawn; to the right, a shed with a half door that we called the horse shed, though I'm sure it never held a horse; to the left, the greenhouse where Dad would grow cucumber vines up one wall and across the ceiling. For a while, he grew cannabis there too, though he told me it was oregano.

That's the sort of house I grew up in, with a greenhouse full of oregano and cucumbers dangling everywhere—and a green budgie named Pansy, after my grandmother, fluttering between everything. When the cucumbers were ripe I'd be sent door to door to sell them, which I hated. The neighbours called me The Cucumber Boy: when I told Dad, he laughed until he had to wipe his eyes.

Dad could never have been accused of being conventional. He was a writer and a jazz musician, so there were two pianos and an electric organ. The pianos were never in tune, which drove Dad nuts; if anyone tried to play them, it made him yell *Jesus Christ*. Then he'd take the front off whichever piano and tighten different bits inside until it was okay, but they always went out of tune again.

He played the organ more than the pianos, one time so loud that the neighbours rang to complain. *Any fucking requests?* is all he said before he slammed the phone down. He went back and played one more tune at top volume, just for good measure.

In the garden, beyond the square lawn, were three apple trees beneath which Mom's radio would crackle in summer from its leather case. It was the only electric thing she brought from the States that worked. I can still see our dog, Teddy, scuttling past wearing a red T-shirt with the slogan 'Curse You Red Baron' on the back. She was buried near the apple tree in that T-shirt.

I hear Dad putting on a Billie Holiday record now; there's a smell of sugar boiling for the beer he made by the barrel-load. I feel the heat of the sun in the turquoise shag carpet of the front room between my fingers now; I stretch on the floor and put my bare feet on the cold tiles of the fireplace.

The thunder of Dad's typewriter through the floorboards of the bedroom upstairs, the rattle of milk bottles as Mom closes the fridge, the clicking of my dog's claws across the wooden tiles of the hall, a sunny day on repeat, all still so clear forty years on.

I've thought of calling to the house a few times since Dad died, and then Mom, just to ask the owners if maybe they'd let me look around. I've made a special detour each time, just to pass by but I never called in.

The house was sold again not too long ago for almost a

million. When I saw the photo online, I noticed that all the trees Dad planted are gone.

All I have left is Dad's old wooden-handled piano tuning tool. It sits on our mantelpiece, a reminder that occasionally things go out of tune in life.

And sometimes the only person who knows how to fix them isn't there anymore.

Nick Cave Nails It

June sees the treacherous bayonets of our garden hawthorn billowing with sweet scented bloom. Its boughs stagger under drifts of them, a snowy confectionery, shuddering under the sun, masking every evil razor point.

It's everything I feel about this month. Celebration and pain. The man who built our fence and tore his hand on one of the barbed branches asked us if we'd let him cut it down, but I told them that I loved the flowers. *Yeah*, he said, *but when they're gone, what are you left with?* He sucked the blood from his cut and raised his eyebrows.

June is a sucker-punch to the gut. I trudge through the summer-soaked city, but it's hard to be sad slipping through crowds with the sun on your face, so I decide not to be, and then I'm not. I just let the feeling sink like a barely visible haze above the hot concrete of some vacant, shuttered flower market that I pass.

Slick with the heat, I slip off the street into a cool bar

to wait for Tommy. By coincidence—because I think we like each other anyway—Tommy was in a play with me last year, Arthur Miller's *Death of a Salesman*. It's a smouldering time-bomb of a story, with little in the way of redemption, a play about false dreams, fragmenting family, and catastrophic loss.

—Cheer up, says the barman. It might never happen.

I'm thinking it already has. Nine years ago and two days ago. *Tick tock*.

Tommy comes in, six foot four, a beard and mirror shades. A few years ago he had long locks of blonde hair that he tied up in ribbons and suspended from helium balloons for a charity stunt. Strangers paid to snip these off and watch them drift away into the sky. It was surreal, like something out of a Fellini film. He raised five thousand. That's Tommy.

I produce the tickets from my pocket like a magician performing a trick. Tonight's Nick Cave gig sold out in seconds so these are like gold dust.

There's fifteen years between Tommy and me; in many ways we couldn't be more different, but there's a happy-sad way about him that I can relate to. I'm able to tell him about this month and what it means to me.

—That's dark, man, he says into his pint.

—It's a long time ago, I tell him. And things are great. I'm really enjoying life right now. The kids are finished school and college for the summer and are job hunting, the house and garden have rarely looked better, holidays abroad are coming up, paid for and circled with scribbles on the calendar. We're even planning a big party.

—I really don't have any reason to be sad about anything, I tell him.

—It's allowed, he says.

The azure sky is still ablaze when we lope out onto the street again and head for the gig. I feel my dark mist dissipating and, strangely, I hold on to it, not wanting it to go, probably because of the hollow I fear it might leave.

At a certain point on the way to the Royal Hospital Kilmainham, we realise that everyone is walking the same direction, then the crowds close in and we flow like human lava through the gates and into the field where the concert stage booms.

There's a tangible crackle as Nick Cave comes on, then we fall into an enchanted silence beneath the throbbing buzz and oscillating Theremin whine of *Jesus Alone*.

You fell from the sky, crash landed in a field, he chants.

Three crows flap high overhead, transected by the contrail of a distant jet that looks as if it's taking off vertically, like a missile.

You're a distant memory in the mind of your creator, don't you see? Cave staggers from one side of the stage to the other, bucking his arms like some sort of undertaker-turned-preacher, while the stage flickers like lightning, and the Bad Seeds writhe behind him on their instruments like enraptured followers.

Cave weaves patterns with his outstretched hands: it's as though he's a sorcerer conducting spells in the air over the crowd as the sun begins to melt around us, an alchemist high on the fumes of transmutation, wringing funk from dirge, gold from lead.

The Japanese call it *Kintsugi*: broken things are mended but the cracks are not only still visible but accentuated with gold. The breakage is celebrated as part of the objects history.

Nine years and two days ago, someone terribly important to me disappeared from the world. He had kept his cancer secret and refused any treatment. I never learned why. I didn't even get to say goodbye. By the time I saw him he was an empty shell.

I've never quite got over it, but I don't know that we're supposed to. We just live with it. When you lose a piece of something, it leaves a gap. You can try to fill it in however you like, even with gold, but it's never really the same again. Eventually, you can learn to see that flaw as a part of the whole and someday find that you hardly notice it.

Nick Cave rails against grief and loss tonight. He takes it and shakes it. It's his invisible dance partner. He coaxes it out of the dark places where it hides like a snake charmer, soothing it one minute, casting it back, screaming, the next.

The last note echoes ominously in the dark.

—So, what did you think? says Tommy.

—I think he nailed it, I say.

Why I Shouldn't be Allowed Out

It's not difficult to find good reasons these days to stay home, close the gate, disconnect the phone and turn up the music, when you're some-one like me—with the uncanny knack of being able to humiliate myself before I've even got to the end of the road.

'That is about as far as I got, one day not too very long ago, when I realised that yesterday's boxer shorts were now working their way in a ball to the end of my trouser leg—a sensation not unlike some small, furry mammal was crawling past my knee to my calf.

That feeling, quite understandably, prompted me to do a small jig on the spot, just as our neighbour came into view, returning in her car from fetching her little girl from school, at the moment my boxer shorts freed themselves and were propelled into the air where they opened like a kite. As my under-things billowed in all their glory for the agonising eternity of what must have been a full fifth of a second, I had the curious sensation of kite-surfing... on a sea of humiliation. Nothing to see here folks, just me high kicking because I thought something was alive in my trousers, then some wretched undergarment floating into the path of your oncoming vehicle.

Inadvertently flinging my underpants at passing neighbours is, of course, only one of my skills. I'm also quite adept at shouting things out the window of our car at friends who I know at least well enough that they'll get the joke, only to find that I've got it wrong, and the person I've just verbally assaulted is a complete stranger.

All good reasons to add a moat to the fence we've just built around the front garden, just to help keep me and the outside world apart for a while. It's a great fence too, not high enough, however, to ensure that I won't mistake someone over it, like the poor young man I thought was our eldest, who I began shouting at in a silly high voice.

—Oh, I managed, finally realising. You're not...

—Nope, he mumbled.

The fence was my wife's idea. The moat is mine. The electronic ankle bracelet, probably an idea our neighbours are conceiving as they draw up a petition.

I fare little better when allowed to wander further afield. The supermarket, for example, is the perfect place to humiliate myself: I have paraded around mine with trouser zips akimbo, or a pair of knickers still stuck to my back with static from the dryer, or enough toothpaste smeared on my face that I looked like a circus employee.

I have charged down an aisle making gorilla noises at a close friend, only to see horror dawning on what turns out to be a stranger's face—and, only yesterday, I duck-walked over to a former neighbour who was staring into a shelf of cheese, only to realise she had just found out about the death of a relative, phone still clutched in her hand.

I have piled three shopping carts high with food that didn't belong to any of them, all in a single trip, once even bagging half a cart's worth of stuff I'd absconded with before realising it wasn't mine at all. I have stood having intimate conversations in line with someone, for at least a few minutes, because I wasn't looking and I thought it was my wife.

This is the man my wife married: the father of her children; he who must be introduced to relatives at Christmas and special occasions; a jester with vertigo dancing on the rim of a silage tank, in splashing distance of everyone who never asked to be entertained.

I am the master of the miscalculated belch and the badly concealed fart; the rock, paper, scissors of awkward handshakes—ready with a friendly fist-bump when a solemn hand is offered, or to reach out and grasp a friendly fist-bump and shake it—and I possess a profound lack of understanding about what level of volume is appropriate at a given moment.

I can regale a table to shocked silence due to content that I haven't metered for the age group present. I have eaten half the wrong plate of food, picked up someone else's drink, and misjudged their ability to appreciate an off-colour joke, and I have done these things sober.

I am the entire reason I must wear sunglasses all the time, for fear of being recognised as *that guy, that time*. It's because of me that I have to change the place where I shop, the route I take, the place where we eat or drink, and I suspect that businesses have folded, that my family and I have had to flee countries, across entire continents, because of me.

It's not easy living with me, and I should know. I'm

the one that has had to live with me the most, and an inordinate amount of that time is spent with my toes curled, arm in mouth, or otherwise in a foetal position somewhere dark, groaning at the memory of some recent error of judgment.

And so, it's for very good reason that I shall mostly be found sitting safely behind my garden fence from now on, hidden behind sunglasses, surrounded by dogs, saying as little as possible to as few people as I can get away with.

It's safer for all concerned—at least until the moat is finished.

Judge Wapner

I have met my fair share of world-famous authors, rock stars, Hollywood actors. I've shared moments with each, however brief, that I will always treasure. I can't say a single one changed my life in any way—except for one.

Long before I saw my name in print, before I could even read, my encounter with one of the biggest television stars of the day would change everything.

Most people have what they consider a first memory. It might be something nice, sitting on my dad's shoulders, or something dramatic, the day my brother set fire to the sofa. But my earliest memory is a little odder. It's of a huge, white building stretching skyward in bright sunshine from leggy palm trees. And I know I was no older than three, because I still have a piece of paper with the date stamped on it.

It was the Los Angeles Superior Court building: there was the smell of polish and the echo of footsteps on tiled floors that seemed to stretch to infinity. It was a terrifying place to me; I cried inconsolably as I was ushered in to what must have been a courtroom; it was there that I came face to face with the man who would change my life, perched high on his bench in a black cape, like some sort of giant human bat.

I was crying because the person I'd seen leaving the courtroom as we went in was a man in a wheelchair: I assumed, as anyone would under the circumstances, that someone would shortly be removing my legs too.

This is the first thing I remember. Not a birthday balloon, or a piggyback, but going to see this giant bat in his white palace to have my legs chopped off. It's indelible. How this shaped me, I can only guess.

The man in the black cape, of course, was a judge, and not just any judge. He was Judge Joseph A Wapner.

Wapner would become famous the world over as the presiding judge on television's *The People's Court*, the first ever courtroom-based 'reality show, made famous again by Dustin Hoffman in the movie *Rain Man*, in which he epitomized the title character with his nervous, autistic ramblings: *uh-oh, 15 minutes to Wapner.*

Back in 1970, however, Wapner was simply a Superior Court judge. He was the son of immigrants from Romania and Russia, a World War Two veteran who'd brought home a Purple Heart and a Bronze Star from the South Pacific, who'd once dated Hollywood actress Lana Turner;. The case before him, on this day, was an application for guardianship and change of name of a three-year-old named David.

I don't recall the rest of the proceedings, but I still have the paperwork—neat legal pages with their numbered paragraphs. At the front is the great golden seal of

California, and Wapner's signature—big, bold and black, across the whole thing.

My maternal grandparents had wanted to adopt me before moving to Ireland from the States, but as my real parents were still alive, one of them would have to show up at the proceedings. No one did, and so only guardianship was granted. However, Wapner did allow the name-change request, and my birth name of David McIntire was changed to David Diebold.

The rest, as they say, is history. It would be some years before I saw my real mother again, and decades before I would track down my natural father using a private detective.

Somewhere in between these things, my childhood happened, and but for that one strange memory, it was largely without incident, unaware as I was that this one day, early in my life, had resulted in my having a different name, one that allowed me to legally grow up with different parents, in a different place.

Wapner retired from the bench in the early 1970s. It was 1981 before *The People's Court* began airing, with its trademark dramatic opening music over which the legend ran: *what you are about to witness is real.*

The show ran for twelve seasons, during which Wapner presided over two thousand half-hour segments. I was in my twenties by the time I discovered the paperwork that related to my brief but formative association with Wapner, and that strange first memory finally dovetailed into place in the jigsaw puzzle of my life.

The grandparents that gave me their surname, signed and stamped by Judge Wapner in a court-room forty seven years ago, died some time ago. Wapner has his own star on the Hollywood Walk of Fame. My almost-adult children don't know *The People's Court*, but I remember it well: it still gives me a thrill to imagine myself gawping up at that same judge all those years ago.

From what I understand, Wapner was a good man, who always sought the most humane outcome for all concerned: if he could get litigants to sort things out between themselves, privately, in his chambers, he often would—once, even on the show, much to the consternation of producers.

I was genuinely sad to hear of his passing at the age of ninety seven, but glad that it was peaceful, by all accounts, at his home in Hollywood: I hope those incredibly tall palm trees swished gently in the night, somewhere nearby.

Me, my half brother, and Bill

Every summer, my half brother comes to see me from the faraway Pacific Northwest of America. He travels all the way to Ireland, a full day's journey of long haul flights and layovers, and he stays in our house with us, often for as long as three weeks.

Summer should be a sad time for us. Our father, Bill, died in Oregon at the height of summer as the blistering heat clawed at his window and cicadas whined underneath the deck outside.

We weren't with him. We were clearing up fallen branches from the other side of the property, wordlessly waiting for a signal from the house which was now the other side of a dried up creek, to tell us he'd taken his last breath.

I didn't really know my brother before it happened. Not like I do now. It's ten years since our father died. Every year, without fail, he's arrived about the same sad time, and we've made sure to really live it up.

I guess that's what brothers do when they want to forget something awful.

Before our father died, I'd only met my brother three times. The first was in Los Angeles, not long after I'd tracked down our father with a private investigator. Before that, I'd no idea I had a sixteen-year-old half brother.

I remember I stayed up late with my father in his hotel room, talking and drinking gin while my brother was stretched out on the floor watching TV. I recall thinking: *That's my only real brother, we're related by blood, how cool.*

At sixteen, he had pretty much left high school and was working with our father building special effects for Hollywood in their own workshop. My father had done well for himself. They were in LA to exhibit at an industry trade show, sharing floor space with make-up artists turning people into monsters and ghouls. To twenty-six-year-old me, it was the epitome of cool.

I remember looking after the booth with my brother while our father was off somewhere and Titanic director James Cameron came over.

—I love your father's work, he said.

Bill reappeared right on time.

—This is my son, he said, introducing me. I was embarrassed because he didn't mention my brother, who stood quietly nearby.

By the time I got to visit my father for the first time on his rambling property amid the fruit fields and nut trees of the vast Oregon countryside, my brother had already started a family of his own. That sounds like a long time, but it wasn't. My brother started young.

You had to enter my father's property through big electronic gates: then the driveway split in two, with one way going up to a huge, two-storey, classic American ranch-style house, the other leading away past a swimming pool, between evergreen trees to the workshop where they worked on their electronics, surrounded by posters of the many movies some of the effects had been used on.

Under the main house was a big games room with real coin-operated pinball machines and a full-size pool table. A door led through plush velvet curtains to a home cinema, complete with surround-sound, vibrating seats and a library of thousands of films.

Our father had put together a room of bunk beds so that my wife and I could stay in the same room as all our kids. I wouldn't have guessed in a million years that this would be the room where I'd one day listen as my father's breathing became a mechanical death rattle.

The next time we visited, because I'd been invited to be an usher at my brother's wedding, it still didn't feel like we knew each other all that well. My brother was the silent type. Our father was loud and filled a lot of space. My brother and I had never played together as kids. I had nothing to tease him about.

When I was leaving Bill thanked me, walking me and my family to our huge American hire-car.

—Inside, I'm already crying, he roared at the car as we trundled off.

The next time I'd see him, he'd be in a coma.

—Are you ready for this? said my brother when he picked me up at the airport.

I wasn't ready. I'd never seen anyone die.

I stayed up all night with our father in the room with the bunk beds. One of them still had a little toy flashlight on the pillow that he had given one of our kids. They must have left it there. There was a button you could press to make it howl electronically like a wolf.

I listened to the hurricane of my father's sick breathing all night, and sometimes I cried to the same rhythm so no one would hear.

He never really woke up. The cancer had already spread to his brain. He'd stopped making sense, then just sort of stopped.

We put pennies on his eyes because we'd heard that this was what you were supposed to do, then we built a bonfire of all the medicines and stuff, and watched the last evidence of that terrible illness go up in flames.

When my brother comes, we hardly ever look back, unless we're real drunk, then I might nod at him and he'll nod back, like we dare to remember.

Storms

Wednesday, and it's almost unseemly, the way the wind peels back the leaves exposing the inner branches of the trees outside. They remind me of women struggling and failing to control their skirts. Car alarms, set off by Storm Ali, taunt them with wolf whistles.

He tore through our garden like a dancing drunk, pushing boxed planters around on their wheels like fairground dodgems. Down the town, a power outage made empty eye-sockets out of shops. The traffic lights were dead, but everyone says how the traffic in the town is smoother when there's no red lights, that drivers are more polite.

My wife phoned to tell me how she'd had to drive around a pair of wicker chairs: it looked as though someone had pulled them into the road to have a chat. Cars had to queue and snake slowly past until the wind levitated them away again.

Storm Ali was on Twitter. Someone posted: *I wonder if I'll get a trampoline tonight by surprise?* Ali replied: *I'm not effing Santa. Be good, get a trampoline. Be bad, get a power outage...*

There were no names for storms when we were kids, they were just gales. They reached under doors, between the seams of windows and made our bedroom curtains billow, then threatened to pop off the top of the house like a tube of Pringles. You could only curl up under covers and wait for the beating to stop.

The early morning after was otherworldly, creeping out to find a day washed and tumble-dried nothing less than thrilling. It was like a baddie had been and kicked our gardens into the streets.

An ancient cedar tree down our road had been so big, you could climb inside. I'd kept comic books stashed up in its boughs. It was split in half, comics gone. I clambered through the wreck, finding branches where before I hadn't dared to go, now felled.

The owner of the tree didn't see me as he shuffled from his house to survey the damage, spitting names I never knew existed for that storm. When he saw me, he shooed me home, telling me it was dangerous. I ran home, smelling of sticky sap for days.

That was forty years ago: the remnants of that tree still stand, the bright wound on its bark long gone. I don't remember another storm like that, the sort of storm you remember when you're age ten, the sort that makes comic books vanish.

The next storm I remember was in the States, when I was working there one summer with the girlfriend who became my wife. To this day, when the wind is strong enough to pick up something and carry it in the air, I'm sure we both think of the same night.

It was a holiday town on the shore of Lake Michigan. We worked as back-waiters in a buzzing waterfront restaurant, meaning we were more kitchen staff than front of house. We worked late and partied hard in free houses and on the beach. Europeans, much less Irish, were a rarity, so when a Londoner working as a child minder in the town, the same age as us, heard who we were, he decided to introduce himself—by climbing on to the roof by our tiny apartment and letting himself in. Gavin became an instant friend. That summer went down in history, not just as the end of the 1980s, but as a long, last blast before attachments and responsibilities: some of the friendships we made would last to this day, others wouldn't.

Some days, you could see a storm coming across the lake for an hour. An approaching front would look like something from a Stephen King story: a creeping edifice over which clouds poured like a waterfall. *Langoliers.*

Other times, a storm might appear out of nowhere. One night, walking home from the restaurant, a wind suddenly whipped up, so strong it tore the plastic covers off all the street lights and sent them shooting past our heads.

I can't remember how we even made it home, just that it was like staggering through a wind tunnel in to which the contents of a hardware store had been emptied. Sparks flew from wires. We shrieked with laughter, unaware the town was being minced.

Next day, power was out everywhere. The radio crackled about people crawling out from storm basements under their houses. We'd just clung together in our one-room rental in a clapped-out wooden house. I'm surprised we didn't wake up in Oz.

Soon after, we took turns driving to Detroit to see The

Cure. Gavin took the wheel on the way home, a relief since I'd recently dreamed we crashed. Gavin was a safe pair of hands. We slept like babies on the vinyl seats, lulled away by the murmur of the motor.

On our last night before returning to Ireland, we took photos of each another at a local beach club: we were wearing war paint, like holiday town warriors, laughing and forming human pyramids on the dance floor.

Gavin planned to stay another year, maybe even for good. I can't remember how long after it was that we took the call, but it seemed he'd crashed a car just outside of town on a long, tree-lined road. He was killed instantly.

It was a while before we made it back. The scar on that hated road had already healed and gone, but down near the shore, where the covers of street lamps had sailed past us that night, a tree had been planted in Gavin's memory: a tree impervious to storms.

I See Dead People

I see dead people. From where I'm sitting, I easily count four. They seem to crowd in, one grinning, another raising a glass of what's probably bourbon. Father, uncle, grandfather, friend. They're all here, jostling for position. Desk space is becoming extremely limited.

It started a few years ago when the dad I called Bill died, and I took a few small things home with me from the house where I last heard him breathe at the young age of sixty two.

I took his Harley motorcycle helmet, leather waistcoat, and the biker gloves that still smelled of his hands, all sun-warmed skin and Eau Sauvage, things that seemed to vibrate in my arms, almost unbearably heavy with his presence. They took pride of place on walls and mantelpieces, quickly joined by photos, enlarged and framed, so that every room I went into made me well with pangs of recognition and remembrance.

When the grandfather I called Dad died, I found a compass he'd used on our hikes when I was nine, the leather on the strap worn smooth from his hands. I took books from his office before everything else was boxed up to be sold—books about jazz and etymology. On one, his fingerprints are still there, on the sticky tape holding the binding together.

These things almost mutter and hum, whistling under their breath just as the strong flourish of his signature dances across their title pages.

Dad's photo, framed, joined Bill's on the mantel, the former admonishing this decision with silent, raised eyebrows, the latter cheekily toasting it from a golf cart with a low-ball glass of Jack Daniels. It was already the longest the two of them had ever been in a room together. Better late than never.

On my desk is a photo from the 1930s of Dad and his kid brother, ankle deep in a tin wash tub and scrubbing down a dog under a hand-pump. The eighty-year-old photo, though sepia with time, is crystal clear. Wet puddles glisten around them, summer leaves in sharp relief against the sky above.

Dad's old Oxford dictionary sits in silent judgement to my left, battered with use (not mine). Behind it is an antique tuning lever, which I can't look at without seeing Dad on his back on the floor, the front of the upright piano removed to one side and him cursing into its ancient, tuneless guts.

There's a stack of books about chess, with hand-notated strategies inside. I never inherited the porcelain chess pieces that went with them, all rich red and alabaster white, carved to look like Normans: pieces I'd squint over, my skinny fists clenched, as Dad cleared his throat from the other side of the board. These scenes play out in the air like holographic films on a loop, over and over. It's emotionally deafening, a cacophony of memories, yet still not enough. Never enough.

As the year just gone unfolded into an entire succession of funerals, I'd rush home to dig in bookshelves or among old photos, haphazard music and films, to find things of significance to the people I'd lost, some of them gifts, some inherited, some borrowed and never returned: each given new priority of place.

I've added books about angling, *The Great Rock Discography*, the French film *Rififi*, all of them propped up like exhibits, whispering to me in the voices of the people who used them.

I have coveted, collected and surrounded myself with these things. They have been my *mementos mori*, reminding me every day of the dead I will never see again, and the death I inevitably face, occasionally to the exclusion of real-life relationships just on the other side of my door.

A stranger walking into these rooms might mistake this collection as the whimsical souvenirs and studies of a man of broad interests. But sometimes I feel like no more than the sum of the people I've known—an empty vessel made of meat, pitifully aching for the company of bones.

This week I attended the third funeral in twelve months of someone I knew and liked. It fell on the first day that I've seen a blue sky, from sunset to sunrise, since I care to remember. I've rarely seen so many funeral-goers so young, so sad and yet somehow, so hopeful, the eulogies seeming to be about seizing life, not dwelling in loss or in pain.

Turning around, away from my crowded desk, I see a face so clear, so beautiful, so alive.

—I'm leaving for my art class, says my daughter.

—Hold on, I tell her. I'll walk you out. I just have to finish a little clearing up.

I watch her turn and leave with a little skip, then I turn back, pick up an empty box, and begin gathering up books watched by picture frames.

Breathless

First thing I recall about the Somme is the cold. I hadn't expected it in March. I wondered if the lads who joined the train at Skerries over a hundred years ago might have thought the same, that France and Belgium, being somewhat more exotic, would be warmer. Instead, bitter doesn't describe the feeling in my dead white hands. I felt as though, if I tripped and fell, my bones might shatter.

The second thing I remember is the silence. Standing at the side of the road by a vast ploughed field near Thiepval, no birds sang. The air, though crisp and bright, hung like a shroud. It dared you to breathe. I felt instantly insignificant. Plunging my hand into the ground on a whim, I plucked a live rifle round from the muck, its unspent contents flowering from one end in a calcified plume.

Looking up, I saw another bullet, then rusted shards of deadly shrapnel, as far as the eye could see. It's known as the *iron harvest* locally, millions of bullets and fragments of armaments working their way out of the dark to the surface of these fields every year, as though the deafening silence wasn't enough of a reminder of the horror that happened here.

The nearby memorial soars like a skeletal cathedral. It was designed by Edwin Lutyens, who also designed the Irish national War Memorial at Islandbridge, where the Wicklow stone survived two IRA bomb attacks with barely a blemish. Freezing, breathless, I made my way towards the towering thing, noting a delicate pattern on its stone surface. Only when I got close did I realize the pattern was made by the names of those who were never found in the surrounding fields—seventy two thousand, three hundred and thirty seven of them, vanished.

My great grandfather was in the US Army Corps of Engineers for the last part of the First World War. I don't know what action he saw, but the name Cambrai rings a bell, just forty five kilometers from the memorial where I shivered. He survived until the 1970s, but had lifelong health issues with his breathing and his skin. Someone said it was an allergy to the wood dust in his workshop, but it's also likely that it was a consequence of his exposure to chemicals on the battlefields in France.

Albert never talked about what he saw or what part he played in that final year of fighting in northern France. My father told me that being in the Corps of Engineers meant his job was to build bridges, though other engineers had organised the first US Army tank units and developed chemical warfare munitions. The details are vague, our connection to that war tenuous.

Strangely perhaps, or not so strange at all, I feel more of a connection to the young Irish men who fought and died, in particular to the ones from the town in north county

Dublin where I have lived for more than twenty years.

Not long before I found myself in cold and silent Thiepval, I'd attended the dedication of a plaque at the gates of Ardgillan Castle, in the hills above Skerries, to two young brothers who had been killed a week apart on the Western Front. As we held a minute of silence on that November day, the trees around us had been busy with the cheerful banality of birdsong.

It was easy to imagine in that moment how the young men, not much more than boys, had craved the adventure of enlisting; their first time away from the farms, let alone overseas. The last thing on their minds would have been the politics of that decision, politics that would result in an entire century going by before they could be remembered with a plaque.

On the way back to our hotel in Ypres, we stopped at a small military cemetery nestled between a rail line and a perfectly circular pond, the crater from some exploded shell. We had all submitted family names to our guide on this battlefield trip to see if any grave of a relative could be found and, as it turned out, there was one right here.

The colleague—whose relative it was—told the story of a granduncle, a Catholic who had fallen in love with a Protestant girl. When the young man's father found out, he marched him to the enlistment office telling him that if he loved their women so much, he could join their army. Just a week after arriving in France, he was killed. No one from the family had ever looked for the grave.

I watched as the man fell to his knees in front of the neat, white slab and, tears running down his face, produced a small wooden cross on which his children had signed their names *with much love*. He planted it in the grass.

Walking back to the bus, our guide pulled me aside.

—You know, I checked the grave records for the name Diebold and found two, he said.

The thought had crossed my mind. My great grandfather had been one of ten children, and his father had been one of ten or more, so there was every possibility…

—One is in an American war cemetery, he told me, the other is in a German one.

In that moment, I was never more aware of the profound futility of it all, that two men on opposite sides of one of the most disgusting wars in history may have been long lost cousins.

I brought home a small stone from a deathly quiet battlefield: on it I wrote the word *Somme*. I kept it for two years: then, on the anniversary of armistice, I made my way to Ardgillan and placed it on a plaque to two young brothers.

Around us, high in the trees, birds sang.

Rube Goldberg's Machine

Are funerals always this cold? I stomp the grey concrete, blowing air halfheartedly between blue lips through the prison bars of freezing fists. The year began as it ends, with a wooden box and a church.

The similarities are dispiriting. The first church also faced diagonally onto two roads. Each church sat in a cheerless cement car park. Each had columns and stone steps around which, once again, we all mill awkwardly.

At that first of three funerals, which was for a work colleague we all liked, I greeted a close friend wordlessly, with only eye contact. We huffed and blew out our cheeks, shuffling icy feet, never guessing one of us would be next. It was cold at his too, less than three months later.

I walked the short route from graveyard to the afters of that one, with another friend, heartbroken but finding bitter humour at some of the funeral service bloopers. When we got to the hotel, we lost each other in the clamor of it all, catching each other's eye just once from where he sat at a table, palms down, cuffs immaculate. He arched his thick eyebrows at me, eyes glittering. I never saw him again.

I meant to visit him in the early summer, when he went into hospital.

—I'll be the one wearing the Simpsons dressing gown and the expression that says, *Did I really give up drink for this?* he joked.

I cancelled. Some simple thing, ridiculously complicated, got in the way. Time just shuddered on. It's not like he was supposed to die.

A certain Rube Goldberg gave his name to machines of ludicrous complexity, designed to accomplish simple tasks. A hen lays an egg that rolls down a chute and hits a spoon which strikes a match and lights a candle to burn the string that holds a knife that falls and cracks open the egg.

How over-designed our lives are, day by day, for something that ought to be so simple.

I look at the box that contains my friend as it arrives for my third funeral this year. For a time, he did what good friends do: he made me feel like I was the only person that mattered. We ate, drank, laughed, and talked about the things we loved.

The box is lifted onto shoulders and carried slowly up the aisle, where candles are already lit, ready to burn through some invisible string, raise the goblet, break the bread, swing the incense and slowly propel the box back out the door and off to wherever they deposit great eyebrows when all their good humour and excellent sense cannot work them any more.

I follow along slowly up the aisle, vision blurring, then I

take my seat, numb. We stand, we sit. Chant, repeat. The clockwork machination of Mass lurches forward.

My mind drifts off mercifully: to the photos he'd shared on his phone; to sunrises through the skeletal trees of Templeogue; to the silver-service coffee and tuna melts we went halves on at Buswells; to his leather gloves on the table with his newspaper, his black scarf and Crombie; to the conversations we became lost in; to his admissions of weakness and encouragements of strength; to a solitary candle in a room.

Click. Whirr. Click.

I don't even know Mass, or at least I didn't before this year, though as a child, fresh off a plane from the States to a school in a corner of Wexford, I sneaked into First Communion classes. At a school service later, my parents were, in equal parts, tickled and horrified as I took the wafer. I was fists and spittle with the disappointment, sure that I was supposed to have been given a mint. And so religion and I parted ways.

There's a time to laugh in church and a time when it is wholly inappropriate, so I hide my face and shake. Someone beside me hands me a tissue and I realise I might just be crying after all.

For a second, I can almost feel my friend nudging me with his knee and confidentially raising a finger to his lips. *Sshh! This is a good bit.* It's not, of course. There are no good bits. Funny guy.

When the coffin is hoisted again and makes its way back down the aisle and I fall in behind it once more, I feel a sick, hollow want to fill with stupid tears and I swallow hard. I'd rather live with it. And I wish it was the same space left by all my losses, just hollowed anew. It's not.

Each death is its own deep hole.

I turn the key in the car and depress the pedal with my foot. Petrol is ignited. Action. Consequence. The Rube Goldberg machine of my life is once again set in motion. Breathe in, breathe out. How many breaths from oblivion are each of us? Ten million? That sounds like forever, but it's less than a year.

In and out.

So we go on.

Click. Whirr. Click.

The Writer and the Banshee

When I was young enough to still be dragged giggling around the kitchen floor by our Labrador, Saul, but old enough to remember every detail of the experience, for a brief, magical time we lived in a strange little house at the top of a cliff. The wind howled almost perpetually around the eaves where it perched, its two dormer windows squinting at the horizon. If the wind wasn't making that lonely moaning sound, it could be so quiet you could almost hear your own heartbeat over the distant hiss of the sea, before the *rat-a-tat-tat* of the typewriter again from the shed where Dad worked.

He had put his career on hold for a year or two—as if I would have had a clue what that meant at the time. All I knew was that to get to our new house we had to drive forever, until the road ended in sand as though washed away by the sea, then a gravel lane you might miss that went up along the cliffs, to where the spray would occasionally shoot through blowholes from the sea below.

A tall boy with red hair opened the gate and handed over keys.

—You're the writer, he said, shy.

—You're Tommy, said Dad.

I still remember how goofy and star-struck Tommy appeared and how funny Dad thought it was. We crunched around the gravel courtyard as Tommy showed us the thatched turf shed and the little storeroom with its single window.

—Perfect, said Dad.

It was a cold house that always smelled like old paper. Aside from a single fireplace, heat came from oil-burning heaters that stank and made your throat burn. Dad spent most of the time out in the storeroom, where you could just see him through the window, hunched over his typewriter. *Rat-a-tat-tat*, then *ding* as the carriage reached the end of a line.

If Dad had a good day, we'd go for a walk, down the lane to the beach beneath the cliffs, where tidal streams carved up the sand in completely different ways each day. Saul would disappear into the distance until he was just a speck, then reappear wet and reeking of some dead thing. Once we found a glass bottle: Dad wrote a note to put in it before throwing it back into the waves.

On bad days, Dad would thunder around growling about *freezing my ass off out there for nothing*, then Saul and I would play in the garden on our own. You could make Saul sit and stay while you went to hide, but he'd always find you because there wasn't really anything in the garden to hide behind, except for half an old sea mine that we'd burn our rubbish in.

We lived so far from anything that you could hear a car

coming for miles. Mostly though, if any came as far as our house, it would mean they had taken a wrong turning. Otherwise there was hardly anyone on our road, except maybe Tommy when he came to cut the grass.

Once, Dad wedged a length of pipe into one of the sea cliff blowholes along the road so that it sounded like someone wailing. This pleased him no end. When he heard that some of the old farmers in the local pub were talking about the Banshee out our way, it cracked him up.

Every day when Dad emerged from his little storeroom, I'd ask him if he'd finished. If it hadn't been a good day, he might say *no, god damn it*. Otherwise, he might say something like *finished for today, anyway*. Then we'd go and check on the Banshee pipe, or to where we could watch the spray shoot through blowholes, or to see how the tidal streams had changed direction.

Winter was hard. The stench of Kerosene from the heaters was so bad sometimes we'd just turn them off and bundle up. Dad visited his storeroom less and less, then took a few night shifts all the way up in Dublin, driving hours each way in the dark in his beaten up old Volkswagen. Christmas came and went and the streams down on the beach changed course a hundred times.

Occasionally, if I managed to pull myself up onto the window ledge with my forearms, I could peer in to Dad's storeroom and see his typewriter there with the empty kitchen chair in front of it, a single sheet of paper trapped in the roller. Once, I remember him opening the door and the wind sending a stack of papers flying into the air and him chasing them all over the courtyard.

I don't think we were happy about leaving when it was finally time to go. I ran around the outside of the house touching things one last time, rough lichens on a dry-stone wall, smooth rust on the surface of the old sea mine, flakes of paint on the frame of the storeroom window, Saul running behind me, barking the whole way.

We stopped just once as we drove out to the lane for the last time, so that Dad could go back and close the gate.

He said we couldn't have a dog where we were going, but there was an old man who lived on a farm who was really lonely since his wife had died: Saul would be very happy there. I still couldn't stop crying. Years later, I suspected that it had been a lie, that there had been no farm—but someone told me that there was, and that Saul had lived to a ripe old age.

We never went back to that cliff top house as a family, but I've been back to look at it with my kids. It's still there, unchanged, caught in time, though I didn't quite have the nerve to peer inside any of the windows.

As a young teenager, I found Dad's book in a drawer, buried under rejection letters from publishers. I couldn't bring myself to read it: I just ran my fingertips over the bumps on the back of each sheet, where some of the letters had almost punched through with the force of his typing, word after word, sheet after sheet, a neat stack of time.

When Dad died and I was asked to look through his little office for the few small things I might like to keep, what I really hoped I'd find was the book, but though I looked everywhere for it, I couldn't find a trace. All I found was a single black and white photo taken from a cliff-top house, of a vast beach carved up by tidal streams, and far in the distance, the tiny black spec of a dog.

Three American Uncles

Many Americans spend years tracing their Irish roots. For some it's a hobby. Others make it their life's work. It's a yearning for something lost or left behind, to feel part of something, to distill the blood down, perhaps, to something finer or more tangible.

Me, I have no Irish ancestry. There's no cottage ruin in Bally-go-something where I can put my hands on the stone walls or bury them in the weeds outside and say 'this is where it all began'. My family tree is American, with more tributaries than the Mississippi, none of them Irish. But I grew up here, chanting *comhrá* at cardboard figures on a felt board in Irish class, slapped by teachers with rulers for not paying attention, going to discos at the local CBS, then sitting the Leaving.

America seemed as far away as the moon, the family history we left behind there, a tantalizing mystery. America was a phone ringing downstairs in the middle of the night,

Mom perched on the first stair with her cigarettes—someone engaged, or jailed, a birth, or a bad accident.

Sneaking to the upstairs landing in the dark, it was like listening in on a late night film. I could only try and fit the grainy images in my mind to the film noir soundtrack of Mom's flint lighter, the tap of her ash, the incomplete script of her exclamations.

I had at least some sense of that faraway cast of characters. Before settling here, we had returned to the States for one long, last visit, staying with two of Mom's brothers. At almost age six, the snapshot memories I'd retained were still in pretty good nick.

Curtis, or *Curt*, a gentle giant with a biker's beard, ran a shop where he sold things he crafted from leather and metal. I remember his laugh and his tattoos. I remember him rescuing me from the pond in his front yard, and the bologna sausage sandwiches he made for me.

Mom's other brother, George, had been a baker, then a ski bum, then a sex therapist. When we went to see him, he lived in a log cabin, among pungent cedar trees.

By the time I began visiting the States, I was a young adult. It was like an episode of that old TV show *This Is Your Life*, with relatives often being carted out at barbecues or produced from behind doors to recount their memories of me, or of my parents, from long before we disappeared. For me, fifteen formative years in Ireland seemed a lifetime. To many in my family, it was a blip.

Curt died young, before I made it back. Uncle George, however, remembered me well. When our first child was born premature in San Francisco, he was hugely supportive. For me, it seemed extraordinary to have family nearby to rely on, people I'd grown up knowing only as a memory, or a barely audible crackle on a phone downstairs.

Once, on a visit to see Mom from Dublin to where she now lived in the Midwest, we took the kids to a nearby playground; we were reminiscing when the gunshot backfire of a car startled us. Mom was clearly unhappy, rolling her eyes as she peered over my shoulder.

I looked around to see a chubby, older man in a baseball cap, shorts and T-shirt, a panther tattooed on each forearm, shuffling over to us with a broad and toothy smile. I assumed it was some annoying neighbor.

—What the heck do *you* want? said Mom.

—Aren't ya gonna introduce me? I noticed the battered, beige car behind him stuffed to the roof with clothes and boxes. Mom sighed. She could barely look at him.

—David and his family are here from Ireland.

—David from Ireland? He thrust a stubby hand at me. Meet your Uncle Bobby!

I guess, in the periphery of my memory, I had been aware that Mom had a third brother somewhere. He'd just never come up much. Turns out he had just arrived having driven from California in three days.

—You can't stay, she told him. The house is full.

—Yeah, but I can at least come over and visit with my nephew today, right? He was unfazed.

Back at Mom's, he called me over to his car.

—Take a look, he said. He unwrapped a greasy bundle to reveal an automatic pistol. Glock, he said. Wanna squeeze off some shots?

—He does *not!* yelled Mom from where she'd been listening behind the screen door.

I might have, but I never got the chance. Uncle Bobby was dispatched to organize alternative accommodation. I think I only saw him once more before we left.

—Don't forget me, he said, handing me a paper napkin

with a smudged email address scrawled across it.

Some time later, Uncle Bobby got a job as a short-order cook in a little diner at the side of the highway, which is where he had a heart attack and died not long after.

As a child, I'd map out the names of my family, after endless quizzing, onto charts, joining the boxes with a pencil. Social media has made us feel a little more connected with family in far-off places, but in reality they remain as intangible as boxes on paper joined by pencil lines.

More than once, I was driven by a need to travel back to where I was from: every time, my family history unfolded before me like a rare and mysterious orchid, one petal at a time, over years—or like the crumpled leafs of a paper napkin found at the bottom of a box of summer souvenirs, with the smudged pen marks of a promise still in it.

Twist for Her, Olive for Him

I often think of Don around this time of year, when the early morning is so dark that you can't see the sea from our windows. It makes me think of the lake, with its icebergs, stretching off into the faint distant glow of what's probably Chicago.

Mom and Don lived just a ten minute summer skip down a tree lined street to the shore of Lake Michigan, where nearby Deerlick Creek trickled onto a hidden beach—perfect for a sundown swim while they minded the little ones, and we watched fireflies drift like embers.

In winter though, there could be six feet of snow. Mom's house was on Blue Star Highway, where roaring snowplows kept things clear, pushing the snow into dirty mountains along the hard shoulder. But you had to shovel your own driveway.

Don was small and sinewy, with a fur-lined hunting hat like something out of Fargo, ice drops forming on his mustache as he scraped black stripes into the driveway with that huge shovel, a slender brown More smoldering in the corner of his lips.

Mom only married Don in 1991, but they'd been in the same high school together, rather like my wife and I, with her barely noticing him and him admiring her from afar. Then World War Two happened.

Don joined the US Marines and served as a Norden Bombsight Technician. When he was discharged, he and his friend found a use for the drop tanks from dismantled bombers and had the idea of making them into paddle boats. They set off to Seattle in an old clapped out Packard with no heating and almost froze to death halfway over the Rocky Mountains.

I only visited Mom and Don twice in winter—the second time would probably have been around now—and Don would tell that same story about almost freezing to death in his car, as we trundled off to the store in his huge 1980s Cadillac, with some jazz station on the radio. The car would bump and grumble along as Don, in padded coat and smelling not unpleasantly of gin Martinis, More Slims and Wintergreen Tums, told me who was on drums, sax, or horns, on whatever number was playing.

He made the best Martinis. Summer or winter, six o'clock was Martini time. Don had run bars for decades—The Downtowner, The Derby, The Dry Dock—and knew how to sling a cocktail. Low-ball glass, full with ice, half inch below the rim with gin, drop of Vermouth, literally, from a dropper.

Mom and Don only ever visited us in Ireland once. It was surreal, like characters from a book or film come to life. What do you do when some of your family seem right out of the pages of a Coen brothers script, and they drop in to you in Skerries for tea? Don helped me unblock the kitchen drain, as it happened.

—It's full of rice and coffee grounds, he muttered from beneath his mustache. Don't you guys have garbage disposal units in the drains here?

I brought him down the town to meet my barman, Terry, in the front of what was then the famous Coast Inn. Terry had run bars in Philadelphia for years.

—Don once booked The Drifters, I told Terry.

—Is dat right? said Terry in his perfect Irish American twang.

I ordered two Martinis.

—Dry. Rocks. Olive, if you got 'em, I told him.

There were no olives and Don was a little troubled by Terry's lenient elbow with the Vermouth.

—Shoulda brought my dropper, he said.

Terry made up for it by letting Don pull a pint of Guinness from behind the counter. It was before the advent of camera-phones, so the only picture I have is in my head, Don behind the Guinness pump, the corners of his mustache indicating a smile.

Those are my only memories of Don over here—so out of context, like snippets from one of those weird dreams you have when you fall back asleep on a Sunday morning—Don taking apart our sink, staring dolefully into his Martini, then pulling a pint.

Maybe it's because I prefer to think of him back home, pottering around the basement between jars of home-grown preserves, his pickles and tomato sauces, or feet up, asleep with Busher the cat and the sports section of the *Chicago Tribune* open on his lap.

It's minus four degrees there today and I bet the lighthouse looks like someone has tried to put icing on it in a wind tunnel. The house on Blue Star would be toasty warm though, even under a blanket of snow.

Mom might be sitting next to the police scanner in that blue rocker sipping black coffee and watching Dr Phil or Ellen Degeneres. If the scanner crackles into life, she might say: oh, that's so-and-so on such-and-such a street again, in trouble again…

Come Martini time, you'd hear the delicious rustle and crunch of Don fishing out handfuls of ice cubes and the tinkle as they hit the glass. Twist for her, olive for him, maybe a little bowl of salty potato chips, or some shrimp and dip if it was on sale at Family Dollar.

He might be whistling some Sarah Vaughan number under his breath, maybe *All Too Soon* with Ben Webster on sax. *You know, his solo was so good*, he might point out, *the rest of the band wouldn't let anyone sit in his seat again, even after he was gone.*

It's ten years since Don slipped in the snow, made it to his favorite chair, and never woke up. When I hear ice clink in a glass, or jazz on the radio, I think of the man who I never got around to calling my step-dad, but who never tried to be anything else than true to what and who he was—just *Don*.

Secrets

I wish I could have back a little of the person I was when I was a kid, around the age of ten, when loyalty meant something as simple as a stray dog following you to school, no matter how many times you told it not to. Then being late rather than leaving him on his own, and enjoying that delicious hollow feeling in the abandoned suburban silence of one minute after nine, sitting on a curb, one arm slung around the dog's neck, explaining why you'd have to go soon. Then spending all day trying to sneak a look out the school window until the teacher yelled, and when two o'clock came, hurrying to be first out the gate to look—but there would be no sign of the dog.

It's not only that different sense of priority I'd like to find again, but an entirely different view of the world, of the meaning of words, of a sense of place,. To a time when fear meant crawling as close as you dared to the edge of the top of the old quarry and looking down to where the chips of stone you let loose clattered across the rock face to their doom; to when all you ever knew about death was a goldfish, inexplicably named Silver, wrapped in tissue, encased in masking tape, and covered in Egyptian symbols done in blue Biro; to the time an ambulance with flashing lights took away Pop Wilkie from down the road, took him away far too slowly, and then never brought him back.

A cruel irony is at work in the universe as time goes by, as the past becomes an island retreating into the distance until you can barely see the stick-figures waving from the shore and no longer discern what it is they're trying to shout to you. If we were as blissfully unaware of ourselves now as we once were, making engine noises as we loped along, sticking an elbow into a jumper to pretend to only have one arm, or picking up bits of old rubbish to add to the horde of bones and bottle caps hidden behind some wobbly bit of skirting board, then we'd probably be placed by worried relatives into a secure institution.

In the house where I spent much of my childhood, every gap or crevice had some coded message or map stuffed into it. Sometimes I'd write *Help, I've been kidnapped. Please, before they... they're coming... helll...* then let the pen run off the page. I deposited these behind radiators or between floorboards, where they'd flutter a few feet through the space and vanish, never to be seen again. I'm sure the subsequent occupants of that house must think that a child was once imprisoned there. Exactly the opposite is true. I was never again as free as in those few short years.

Mom suffered spells of terrible depression, occasionally characterized by long afternoon naps that you disturbed at your peril. She'd leave out a packet of tomato Cup-a-Soup, a glass of milk and three cream crackers. I'd let myself in with a key knotted around my neck on a nylon cord, the kind that might strangle you a little as you stretched up to unlock the door.

I'd carefully pour the milk down the sink, hide the packet of soup and take the crackers, jamming one into my mouth and breathing through crumbs as I carefully wrote a note: *back at dinner time*, then I'd creep out, pulling the door after me and wincing as the lock snapped. I'd duck around the low wall and try to get to the top of the road using only the neighbours' gardens, pulling myself along on elbows across lawns. Someone banged a window.

—Aren't you a bit old for that?

It was the beginning of the end.

On the wooded hill nearby, I had a network of forts, intricately mapped. I remember marking one area on a map *Here Be People* as though people were monsters.

All these years on, I still know where those forts are, their roofs of interwoven twigs long since caved in upon the bones, bottle caps, and plastic sandwich bags of maps. I'm afraid to look there now, and I'm not sure if that's because they might still be there—or that they might not.

One of the last times I visited a hidden fort was on the birthday before Mom first left us to go and live in America; I remember her struggling through the bracken behind me as I cajoled her along, telling her it was just a little further.

When we got there I could see it through her eyes. The magic evaporated. It was just twigs and rubbish in the hollow between a boulder and a tree.

It started to rain on the way home. After we got back, Mom caught me crying into the pillow in my bedroom. I couldn't find the words to tell her that the reason I felt so sad, so heartbroken, was because I had the feeling that I had given up a secret, one that was lost forever.

Author's note

I haven't changed any names in this book, nor have I intentionally airbrushed anyone out, though there are close relatives or friends on the fringes of many of the stories, often in the same room, who I felt would needlessly complicate things to include. As it is, many of the stories happen at different times, in different countries, with entirely different branches of family, and I know this can be confusing. I've had two mothers, three dads, and all the half siblings and step siblings that go with that. Believe me, it's enough trouble keeping up with who's who myself—but, well, that's just life, and families. I hope you can get your head around it all quicker than it took me, which is most of fifty two years. Anyway, take it that nothing here has been intentionally conflated, compressed or contracted, to the best of my knowledge—each piece is as true an account as I can remember, and it isn't my intention to hurt anyone's feelings for all that.

Diary of a Wimpy Dad

DAVID DIEBOLD

e-Book now available
at amazon.co.uk

Monument Media
Dublin, Ireland

My Son's Eighteenth Birthday— and I'm Not Invited

—Nuts? I ask, holding up a pack and cocking an eyebrow. We've driven miles to a supermarket for party supplies. It's our eldest son Zachary's eighteenth—which is all, well, rather awkward, as it happens.

—I mean, I *remember* being 18. I'd confided this to my wife earlier, screwing up my face as I emphasized the word 'remember' to show how inconceivable it seemed that one of our children should already have reached the milestone.

—Don't be silly, my wife replied. Of course you don't. But I did. I do. What I don't recall is getting older. Zachary shrugs at the nuts.

—Sure, he says, so I toss in two packs.

—Onion rings? I inch the cart forward.

—Cashews? My wife chimes in, enthusiastic.

Thing is, we could spend all day perusing the snacks, but there's no avoiding the elephant in the middle of the aisle as the booze section yawns open ahead of us.

I catch my wife's eyes and steel myself, sucking in a single deep breath between clenched teeth before doing what I feel is the only appropriate thing under the circumstances.

I fling myself onto the cart, arms wide and shoot off in the other direction.

—Wheeee!

Sometime later, still throbbing a little where my wife may have thumped me, I find myself loading two small flatpacks of Heineken into the boot of the car.

—Perhaps it would be good, she tells Zachary, if we were to just hold on to one until you need it.

—Sure, he shrugs again.

—Where will we be for all this, again? I ask.

—In the playroom, she says.

—The playroom. All night

—Yes, she says. All night.

I swing the last bag in.

—How much was this lot again?

—One hundred and ninety euro, she says.

I splutter a little.

—Seems like a lot of money, I mutter to the dashboard as I reach down to turn the key. For a party in our own house that we haven't even been invited to.

By eleven o'clock that night the house is heaving with teenagers beyond the playroom door.

—It's good we're here, says my wife. You know. Just in case… The sound of live music begins now from where they've found the drum kit and my electric guitar.

—Um, I'm going to the kitchen for beer, I announce.

—Eh… she begins, but I'm already squeezing down the hall past young men, most of them taller than me and eyeing me dubiously. I almost explain myself but decide to just press on instead.

I shuffle through the hubbub, nodding politely, but I only seem to make people tense.

—Hello, Mister-Zachary's-Dad, says someone, dry as ashes. I pop my head in at the band, who promptly drop everything and apologise.

That's when it hits me. I am the Party Killer.

—You're back quick, says my wife before adding, mock-sympathetic: Did no-one ask you to join in with a jam session then?

We listen as the party peters out and then we emerge to clean up while Birthday Boy walks the last of his buddies home. Room by room, we examine the debris like a forensics team.

—Someone had a coconut, I observe, sweeping up bits.

We examine gifts, some of them so grown up, like a collection of Oscar Wilde quotations; and some of them some not so grown up—monkey-face slippers.

I'm emptying half-full beer cans down the sink as I feel a twinge inside my chest somewhere at just how grown up our boy suddenly seems. And us, still here, waiting in the wings, *just in case*.

Looking back at me from the window above the kitchen sink is me, still feeling young enough to want to join in— yet so genuinely old for the first time…